8235

THE CHAFFINCH

WANDERINGS WITH THE WOODMAN

by

Hugh Brandon-Cox

With black-and-white illustrations
by the author

The Thames Publishing Co.,
Ludgate House, 110/111, Fleet Street,
London, E.C.4

CONTENTS

CHAPTER I

Adventure Ho!

" Waggon wheels, waggon wheels,
Keep on turning, waggon wheels."

Tunelessly, because my singing voice is like a frog's, I sing snatches of this song as the red wheels of the caravan turn slowly on the country road.

It is April; the day is mild, with that lovely feeling of spring in the air. From out of the hedge by the roadside a robin sings with a gay and much more merry note than is evident in his little autumn song, and everywhere I look across the fields I see signs of new life.

The harness jingles and the caravan creaks. Robby pulls as though he knows we are bound for adventures on the open road. Toby, my faithful dog of many breeds, with a pure white coat and one black ear, rests his nose between his paws and looks with intelligent brown eyes at the way ahead.

But wait a bit! Our party isn't complete yet, for we have to pick *you* up. *You* are to make the fourth " good companion " on this journey of ours.

Oh, I know you are excited! Not only have you the Easter holiday in front of you, but you are all packed and waiting, with haversack filled and checked many times with my list of things to bring. Mother was just a little bit nervous of your coming at first, wasn't she? But after a while she said " yes," and she has packed in a tin of those lovely home-made cakes and scones she treats us with on Sunday when I call to see you.

" Whoa, Robby! Here we are, and our young friend is as eager to be away as we three are."

7

Mother flusters around, making sure nothing has been forgotten in your kit, and then with a wave we are off. The last of home we shall see for a bit is Mother's handkerchief waving us goodbye as we round the bend in the lane.

You breathe in deeply with excitement. You have your little note-book all ready to start making notes of everything we see. You have been reading about wild life all the long winter, and now you have the chance to come with me and really see and watch some of those birds and animals whose struggle for life has so excited you in your reading.

At last you will begin to feel that fine thrill of getting beyond the covers and diving deep into the wonderful book of the fields and hedgerows.

You'll probably start, as I did, by jotting down all the exciting little happenings you see on our first day out, and other interesting little tit-bits, and gradually you will find that this habit will grow on you until your jotting-books become prized possessions. You will most likely try your hand at sketching, too. Oh, I know that you are pretty good already, although you are so fond of telling me that you can't draw a straight line. For your consolation I would say, " Just you *find* me a straight line in nature, and *I'll* be pleased to draw it! " No, don't give up hope because you were not born to be an artist! Just put down roughly what you see and feel, and even these little scribbles will mean a great deal to you later on and you will get better all the time.

Maybe you have always lived in a big city or town, and feel that *you* can't see much; but I wonder. For instance, did you ever hear what to my mind is the loveliest thing about early spring, the return of the wonderful dawn bird-chorus, when thrushes, blackbirds, chaffinches, robins and wrens, and many others, seem to strike up as though they were all part of some gigantic choir, pouring into the air a song of pure joy for life? You have to get up *very* early to hear that, when it is still darkish, but with the first streaks of light appearing in the east.

" Ugh! " I can hear you say. " Fancy getting up so early! "

But just brave it one quiet morning and listen. First, you will hear a solitary " Cherry-tree, cherry-tree, cherry-tree! " repeated three times, followed by an impatient " Hurry-up, hurry-up, go-to-it, you'll-do-it, you'll-do-it! " and you will be hearing the song-thrush calling the others. Then in come the beautiful, liquid notes of the blackbird, up and down the scale, to be joined by the whole range of small songsters, with the tiny, brave jenny wren gaily making up for its lack of inches with the sheer joy it puts into its powerful little song.

The whole chorus goes on until the east looks quite light, and then, as suddenly as it began, it dies away and all is quiet for a time, as the birds search for their breakfast. You can hear this chorus even in the largest town, and so long as you have a small patch of garden with a tree, there you will find the song thrush, perched on the very topmost twig, ready to sing and sing for the sheer joy of living.

Then when you are out by yourself for a walk there are always little nooks and corners where birds *will* gather. Once you start watching you will find yourself trying to put words to some of the calls you hear, and very soon you will say to your companions knowingly: " There goes a yellowhammer. Hear his ' Little bit-of-bread-and-no-che-e-e-s-e '." He says this quite plainly, the last word sounding like a rusty gate swinging on its hinges in the wind.

Of course, for you lucky country-dwellers, and for you hardy ones who live on the moors or near the coast, the study of the habits of many more creatures is possible; but wherever you live this little island of ours will provide you with all the wild life you will want to learn about, and I hope that you will come along with Toby and me as we roam the lanes and marshes in the evening's fading light, in the early morning, and perhaps in the darkness and mystery of the long night hours.

We have travelled a long way since early morning now, and I think we will unharness Robby and settle here by this stream for the night.

I know you love sitting round a crackling log fire when it is very dark in the countryside, your eyes fixed on the little patch of glowing wood, and feeling that drowsy glow of enjoyment of everything around you. Well, so do I, and we are in no hurry on this journey. Let us just sit here for a bit while we watch the coffee in the pot boil and sizzle on the embers. A few spots of rain strike the fire with a " fizz," but it doesn't mean much—just the usual stray drops we so often get on a spring evening. Leaning against a tree-trunk it is easy to dream, isn't it?

Toby gazes unwinkingly into the fire, seeing some fat rabbit, for a certainty. I—well, I'm just dreaming of how good the earth smells at night, and how I'm the richest man

JENNY WREN

in the world when I'm so close to nature and free to wander where I please for a short while. And you? Well, of what are you dreaming? You were just seeing pictures in the fire, and finding that your mouth was watering for some of that sweet-smelling coffee, and a taste of the damper you are watching me make! All right, then; pass along your cup and plate, and maybe tomorrow night I'll show you how to make a damper, too.

Sure it's good to be alive out here together like this, with no sounds but those strange ones of the night. Before we finish this trip you must learn to make a few useful articles for yourself out of the things you find lying handy. I'll soon teach you.

"Well, I guess it's time to turn in, Toby. Come on, old chap; that rabbit will wait until tomorrow."

The fire glows lower and lower. The ashes begin to show white. It is very quiet.

Suddenly, sounding as if it were right on top of the caravan, comes a piercing, high-pitched, screaming cry—the hunting call of the barn owl. All round in the undergrowth small bodies rustle deeper into the leaves for protection against the steel-like talons of this killer of the night. I glance out of the caravan just in time to see the owl settle for a moment and then fly upwards with a mouse dangling from its vice-like claws. Without a sound it went, a ghost-like form, white of face and with huge eyes set deep in the white down around a wickedly sharp beak. The wings and back are a lovely yellowish-buff colour, and, being soft and rounded, it makes no sound as it glides through the air, always searching with those piercing eyes for a victim below.

You know, "Screecher," as the barn owl is commonly called by country folk, *can* see in the daytime, probably nearly as well as you or I, but its eyes are more adapted to the soft light of the dusk or early morning, when mice and rats try to make merry at the expense of the farmer's grain. It takes wonderful eyesight to pick out the swift-moving form of a mouse sliding through the grass; but watch with me for a bit as we follow an owl's flight in the dusk and you will see it suddenly brake without warning and drop without a sound. Off it goes with its victim, which has its back broken by the steel-like claws, and when it reaches its favourite perch—tomorrow we'll have a look at that old spruce fir I was telling you about earlier this evening, if you will remind me—it swallows its meal whole. It doesn't even bother to skin the mouse or other victim; down goes the whole meal in one huge gulp. This performance is conducted with much shaking of the head and blinking of the huge eyes, and then follows a short rest. After a few hours the undigested portions of the meal are thrown up in the form of grey pellets; tomorrow we'll try to find some of these and have a closer look at one.

The brown owl is not letting Screecher have the hunting to himself tonight, however, and his quickly repeated call note, " Keek, keek, keek," and the long trembling, " Too-hoo-hoo," echoes across the field.

You would scarcely think of a brown owl as a pet now, would you? But the fact remains that brown owls can be tamed and are very intelligent. I had a youngster, about a fortnight old—all eyes, he looked— a few years back, and I reared him. He became wonderfully tame and never left my shoulder when I went on an evening country hike. I think I scared a good many people with this fierce-looking pet, who used my ear to steady himself with his sharp, hooked beak; but although he could have given me a very bad bite he just held on very gently. " Joey ", as I called him, was a solemn little bundle of tawny down, with large round bluey eyes, when I first had him. Feeding him was a problem, for although I could get pieces of meat, owls must have something rough to help their stomachs, and I had to get my friends to help by giving me any mice they caught. Young birds that had fallen from the nest and died of cold were also taken. William, the cat, was a help, because he caught a good many mice and brought them all to me, which is something very unusual for a cat to do. During the daytime, Joey would sleep peacefully in the coalshed—he would never enter a cage— but in the evening he would come out and ask for his supper. It was very amusing to come up behind him, for then he would turn his head right round, without moving his body, and look at me " with eyes at the back of his head ". If he was ever frightened he would draw up his

BARN OWL

whole body very stiffly, stand high on his legs, and make his eyes as slanting as a Chinaman. He was very clean, and often bathed in the basin of water I gave him.

It was not until I went to France, to watch some of the wild creatures there, that he left me, and I shall always miss him.

By day, we can find the brown owl asleep in an old hollow tree, but the barn owl lives up to its name and favours barns and church-towers. Owls lay almost round, pure white eggs, placed on a roughly made nest of a few twigs and pellets, and if we do happen to discover one—well, just watch out that one of the parents doesn't see us near the spot, or we shall be given a very warm reception, for owls are no cowards and fight with great courage to protect their eggs and young. Young barn owls look like balls of cotton-wool, but just try to pick one up and you will soon discover they are not so innocent of weapons as they seem at first sight!

In the darkness the owls move away from around the caravan, but there remain other queer sounds. Rabbits will thump as they constantly nibble the grass, leaving a few bucks always on guard. Even though they are quite a good way from us, sound carries a long way through the ground, and having an ear close to the earth we can hear these noises as though they were magnified. Anyone who has had a good deal of country experience knows the old dodge of listening with an ear close to the ground to hear distant noises.

Toby sighs deeply and dreams away. I wish we really knew the thoughts of a dog. They *do* think deeply, I know.

You are feeling restless, as we all do on the first night under the slender covering of canvas that shuts out the great arc of the sky above. It is drizzling, with fine, soaking rain, or I would not be hiding my head from that grand sight. How lovely it is to lie and gaze upwards in the small hours of the night, look into the velvety darkness of the far-distant heavens, and watch the tiny points we call stars. There is no moon tonight, just a luminous light, for it is very rarely that we find a *really* black night.

Do you feel lonely with me now? No? I thought not! Just beginning to catch the thrill of the great outdoors, eh? You are in the first stage of catching the finest, healthiest love of all, the love that grows in *me* more each year, the deep-rooted love of nature and of everything that is born, that fights and that dies under the roof of the stars that we see above us.

How many times do we hear people say, "I hate the winter; everything is so dead and miserable!" I think I hear it nearly every day when the weather turns really cold, but you and I—well, we shall not talk like that, for we will go through the year together and you will find that even in the very dullest, quietest month exciting little adventures will happen to us.

I'm *so* glad you can follow the year with me and that you want so much to know something about it. We'll have a grand time if you just keep close to me, and when I say "quiet" be quiet! Doing that, we shall see so much that we should otherwise miss. Never forget, will you—in fact, write it down in your notebook and underline it—that when you want to watch a wild animal or bird keep absolutely still and stay in the same position for as long as you can? If you *do* move, change your position very slowly and without any jerky movement. I know that "I've jolly well got cramp in my legs" is about the first thing you will tell me, but remember this little bit of advice, won't you?

Hey, steady there, now! You mustn't jump like a nervous horse at that noise! But I know that the scream of a vixen, the fox's mate, *is* pretty terrifying the first time you hear it in the darkness, as she calls her handsome male. The chestnut, dog-like fox is a real killer of the night, and every man's hand is against him. Sometimes I feel sorry for him when I watch a pack of hounds hot on his scent in the autumn, followed by the red-coated hunters. It's one of those things we always feel, isn't it, that sympathy for the one who has the odds against him? But when I think of all the fowls that are left lying about, killed by his sharp, snapping jaws, then I do not feel so tender-hearted!

Answering the vixen comes the sharp bark of the fox. He

BROWN OWL

barks quickly, but not for long, as he doesn't want to advertise his whereabouts. Silently he glides through the undergrowth, intent on the search that keeps all wild creatures busy for the whole of their all-too-short lives, the search for food.

Softly, mellowed by distance, come the notes of the village church clock, striking away the night hours. Like a sentinel the church stands above the rest of the village, and from its belfry have flown an army of bats to search for their supper. Feared and treated with dread the world over, the bat has been at the root of some of the weirdest stories of the night. The people who live in the mountains of Germany greatly fear the great vampire bats. In those lonely, desolate regions it is a brave man who ventures out at night, so steeped are the local people in old folk tales. We are not *quite* so stupid as to fear these delicate little flying animals with the mouse-like body and skin-like wings, are we? But they always bring a sense of the uncanny, and in some of my wanderings in the remoter parts of our countryside I have put up for the night with people who warned me against leaving my window open for fear of bats!

Watch a tiny pipistrelle, that small bat we usually see in the lane at dusk, chasing a moth, and you will say to me at once: " Why on earth do we say ' blind as a bat '? He must see jolly well to follow that moth in this light! "

Well, bats do not have to rely on their eyesight as we do, and they have the most amazing, delicate set of nerves and fine hairs situated on the sides of the muzzle, on the ear-trumpets and on the wings. They have huge ears, by the way, and as for the wings, they are worth a close study. Ending in four human-like fingers, they are used to grip the barn or church wall from which the bat hangs, head downwards, all day. The skin of the wings is very strong, with light bones, and although on the ground it is the picture of clumsiness just watch the wonderful way in which it misses every obstacle in the air, and follows every movement of the moth.

The bats' squeak as they fly is so high-pitched that many humans cannot hear it at all. It is believed that the nerves on the wings are so sensitive that they receive very quickly the vibrations of the bat's flight reflected from the object near by, so that the bat has time to swerve away.

It has a huge mouth, filled with sharp little teeth, and can pick up insects easily whilst in mid-air. During a spring or summer evening bats perform a fine service to the farmer by ridding the air of countless pests. As the cold weather of late autumn approaches, however, they gather in groups and fight for the best cracks in the barn or tower, where they will hang in a death-like sleep for the long winter months, waking once more when the spring air stirs. Even if they could stand the cold of winter, there would be no food for them, so nature makes them hibernate, or sleep for months on end, and during this time they exist on the fat which they have managed to store in their tiny bodies during

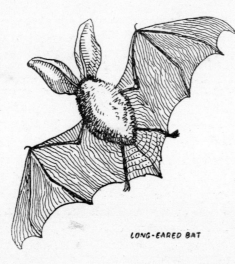

LONG-EARED BAT

the summer. The little heart *just* beats, but if you find a bat in a cobwebby corner in mid-winter you will probably think it is dead.

We have about twelve types of bat in this country, and some are fairly large, one being about twelve inches across the wings.

I remember as a boy staying in a house in a Midlands town. In the very early hours of the morning I was awakened by a great commotion. A bat had flown through an open window into a bedroom, frightening the woman occupant almost out of her wits. Many townsfolk shrink from even the most harmless of wild creatures at close quarters. This bat kept the whole household awake for hours, for search as we might we failed to find it, and the lady it had disturbed refused to go back into the bedroom until the invader had been banished. The bat, however, could not be located, and the general opinion was that it had found its way out of the open window again. This notion was proved wrong, for next evening the bat came out from wherever it had cunningly hidden itself, having defied all search.

I guess we will leave the bats to their nightly flights for the present. I have dreamed the night away with idle thoughts, as I do so often. You sleep peacefully. Now that dawn is at hand the creatures of the night silently disappear and those of the day return once more.

HERON FISHING.

CHAPTER II

Discoveries in the Wilds

BREAKFAST UNDER A ROOKERY—A MORNING'S WANDERING—ROOKS, JACKDAWS, AND STARLINGS—THE BIRD URCHINS AND THE OLD GENTLEMAN OWL—THE KILLER STOAT—FARMHOUSE FARE

We certainly did not need an alarm-clock at our camp this morning, did we? Our caravan is right under a rookery, and now above us the noise is deafening.

"Caw, caw, caw, aah, caw!" So it goes on, and mixed with the cries of the rooks comes a deep "honk, honk", which keeps on as if it were a taxi-horn that refuses to stop. The two noises shake all the sleep from us, and as you gaze upwards at the mass of forms overhead you can't help saying, "Whatever are those huge grey birds like storks flying above the rooks? Aren't they big!"

I am glad we stopped here, for I shall not often get the chance of showing you the home of the heron, that slow-flying, slate-grey bird we sometimes see standing so very still gazing into the water by the river-bank. The heron is our tallest bird, and is a wonderful fisherman. He has very keen eyesight and will stand for hours watching and waiting. When a fish passes, down will stab his very long, sharp, greyish-yellow bill, and out of the water flashes the catch—the grey fisher has earned his supper.

But he wants his breakfast, too, and we are just lucky to be able to watch him near us as he fishes in the stream.

Now keep quite still, will you? See that thin black crest curling half way down his neck, and those long thin legs?

Suddenly, in the early morning sunlight, there is a flash, and out of the water is pulled an eel. Striding to the bank of the stream, the heron bangs the eel hard against a stone until it is quite dead, then, tossing it into the air, he catches his meal and gulps it down whole.

16

Jot down in the notebook, will you, that the heron will eat frogs, fish, water voles, newts, snails, large insects, and even young waterfowl? So you see he is pretty easy to please with his food.

The lonely heron we sometimes see flying along a marshy canal has usually been turned out of the herony because of some crime. You know, birds and animals often have a strong sense of what is right and what is wrong, and one of the family who breaks any of the rules is turned out to lead a lonely life. Crime definitely does not pay in their world when their neighbours find out!

See those huge, black-looking nests high above us? Herons build in the very tops of slender trees, usually round a pond, and lay large, pale, greenish eggs. When there are youngsters on these platforms the noise is pretty awful, but what always amazes me is how the eggs stay up there during the very windy weather we have in spring.

The untidy nests of the rooks look much smaller, don't they? I'll be willing to bet that the farmer who owns this land has some pretty strong words to say about these black villains when they get among his newly sown wheat in early spring.

If you had been born in the country not so many years ago it is very likely that as soon as you were old enough to be trusted you would have been given some thick chunks of bread and cheese and a gigantic rook-scaring rattle, and sent out into the fields all day to keep off these robbers. Maybe you wouldn't have minded not going to school, and getting a few pence at the end of the week for your work, but there are many well-known men today who started by getting simple books and trying hard to understand them when they were alone rook-scaring.

Often, however, rooks are not so black as they seem, for if we look at young oats they have pulled up we can often see that each one has contained a grub, which if left alone could have destroyed the crop.

Of course, they *do* do a lot of damage, for they eat much newly sown corn, and birds' eggs, and will even pull grain out of the stacks when they are very hungry. But they also destroy so many wire-worms—those thin, white little pests you simply *must* get out of the garden—snails, slugs, maggots, and other grubs of all kinds, that many farmers have a good word for them.

You remember last evening how you kept hearing those big brown cockchafer beetles whirring by the fire? Well, they usually come out in the evening, and the rooks do a great deal of good by eating the grubs of this beetle when they find them buried underground, where the female beetle has laid her eggs. These hatch out in a few weeks, and grow into fat, dirty-whitish grubs, which live under the soil and feed on the roots of grasses and plants for *three* summers. Even when the grub becomes a beetle it is still a nuisance, for it eats leaves, and I remember when I was in France having a gigantic swarm of these cockchafers settle on the oaks in the grounds of our old shooting-lodge. In a few days they had stripped them of their leaves. It was a very unpleasant thing to walk in the garden in the daytime, for every now and then a plump beetle would drop down from the branches above! It was even worse when we lit the lamps in the evening though, and we could not have any windows open because of the whirring swarm.

ROOKS

Starlings love the grubs, which is a good thing, and the velvety mole relishes them. Bats will also hunt and eat the beetles, too.

There are a good many youngsters in the rookery now, for even in early February they were repairing the old nests and laying their pale, greenish, black-spotted eggs. They use the same nests year after year, just adding to them, but about September they leave the rookery and go to pine and beech woods to sleep. Back they come at the first signs of spring, however, and that is why I always think their cawing is such a welcome sound.

Crows do not live together like rooks. They live in pairs, and build in the top of some high tree away from houses. They are very unpopular with the poultry-farmer, because they will swoop down and make off with some of his young chicks as soon as his back is turned.

Can you see how the rooks have large bald patches on their heads above the beak? Well, they get this at about a year old, and this makes them easily known from a crow.

While we have been chatting like this about the rooks we have not been idle, for that would be a poor way to start off this lovely calm morning. The dead ashes have been raked out, and now a cheerful little fire is glowing and crackling merrily, for I laid in a handful of twigs so that they would dry overnight. Always remember that we have *very* heavy dews in spring and summer, so that it is no use looking for dry twigs first thing in the morning!

There is a delicious smell from the frying-pan. Now you have your notebook out, and before you fill that empty space in your stomach, just jot down how to make a damper, will you ? Then perhaps you can try your hand tonight. It is very easy, for you merely take some flour and mix with water to a firm pastry, and then add a pinch of salt. Now you can either pull this out into strips and twist it round a twig you have previously peeled and heated, turning it round in the ashes until it gets a delicious golden brown, or you can make it into a pancake and lay it in your tin plate. Then you fix the plate upright before the fire and bake the damper brown on both sides. In either case, you have some lovely pastry when spread with jam, syrup or honey.

While we are having breakfast do you notice how in the field opposite there is now a really big gathering of rooks, starlings, and jackdaws feeding. The jackdaw, who says " Jack, jack ", quite plainly, is rather smaller than the rook and has a distinct grey patch on his head. He nests in hollow trees or church towers, and is a lively, intelligent bird. I had a jackdaw pet for a long time, and his only " crime " was that he simply could not resist carrying off anything bright I left about. All small objects of a shiny, bright nature attracted Jack, and he had a hiding-place full of little odds and ends he had hoarded away. He picked up a good many words, which he imitated quite clearly.

Now, if we want a really clever little mimic we shall not have to look further than those starlings. Although from a distance the starling appears to be blackish, with a mass of light spots, when the sun catches his feathers he is a mass of bright, changing, reflected colours, and looks very attractive. He walks about, the same as a rook, whom he follows closely, for while the rook will turn over the ground with his long beak the starling only picks off the grubs that are left above ground with his sharp yellow beak.

Do you remember how you thought you had heard the cuckoo very early in the spring, long before it really arrived here? Well, that was the starling just having a little joke on you. He will perch on the top of a tree or on a house roof, and after warming up with a few of his own notes, which sound just like " whew, whew, wheew ", he will launch out into a series of brilliant imitations of other birds, mocking the lovely notes of the thrush, the blackbird, the lapwing, and many others.

The starling is now our most common bird, and sometimes we shall see vast flocks of them in the late evening as they settle for the night. Any hole in house, barn or tree will serve for a nesting site, and the poor old woodpecker often has to chip himself another hole when he comes back to find a pair of starlings in possession of his site. An untidy mass of grassy material is bundled together, and in this are laid the lovely pale-blue eggs. The starlings keep up a terrific chatter all day, and when the youngsters add their voice then Mother usually wishes they were anywhere but nesting under the eaves of the house.

The dew is rapidly leaving the grass, and Robby is waiting patiently for his harness, for he thinks we are off at once. But first I want us to go for a morning walk back to that spruce-fir we passed yesterday, where we noticed the owl's pellets.

Here we are, and just in time to see a rather amusing little happening, which takes place every time an owl is found resting during the daytime by his smaller bird enemies. The first one to spot him gives a yell to call up every other bird in the neighbourhood, and within a few moments there are a noisy chattering gang all intent on getting their own back on the owl for his night work. Being a sleepy individual during the day, he takes no notice for a bit, but the noise soon worries him, and off he flies,

STARLING

slowly flapping his wings and pursued at a respectful distance by a crowd, who look like a gang of street urchins after an old gentleman!

You've found some of those pellets, have you? Well, break one open, and you will see that inside are bones, fur and feathers, all the parts of the meal which were not digested. If the meal was a mouse, all the small bones will be found in the pellet, and the fur also.

Well, let's start back, shall we? We don't want to waste too much time. On the way

back try to tell me some of the
birds you see.

" By the way," you say between bites of one of Mother's
scones, " what causes a bird to
cast up its food like the owl? "

Well, slow down a bit and
I'll explain. You see, birds
have no teeth, but in most cases
the food they eat is ground
up in the gizzard before being
digested. This gizzard has
tough sides, which keep rubbing against one another, and
the bits of grit you see fowls
picking up are lodged in this
gizzard and act as small grind-
stones, crushing up the food.

THRUSH AT "ANVIL"

But if the prey is swallowed whole, as with an owl or a hawk, the poor
gizzard cannot cope with bones and fur. So these are thrown up again.
After a meal an owl will settle itself on its favourite perch, and some
time after, when the food has been broken up by its strong stomach
juices, it gets rid of the parts it cannot digest in this manner.

Oh, yes; here is another interesting thing, too. See this stone covered
with broken snail-shells? Well, it's an anvil for a thrush, and you can
often see them. You see, the thrush is *very* fond of snails, and when it
finds one it will bring it to its favourite stone and hammer away until
the shell comes away in pieces. Down goes the soft tasty snail, and off
goes the thrush for more.

There will be plenty of jottings for the notebook on the way back to
the caravan, and I see you have jotted down some of the more common
birds, but wait a minute—here is something really interesting.

See that queer little animal jumping up and down and turning somer-
saults in the field there? He hasn't seen us because of this bush, but
watch him closely and see what happens.

I have a hard job keeping Toby quiet, for he can see the small form and
wants to be off.

" What is it? " you say after a bit.

Because I can see the black tip to its tail I know that it is a stoat, one of the most deadly little killers we have. Chestnut-brown in colour, it has almost white underparts. It will kill a rabbit or even a hare by a vicious bite at the back of the neck, where it punctures a vital artery.

Now watch closely, because the stoat isn't jumping about like this merely for fun. Oh, no! Quite near him is a rabbit, staring fixedly at the whiskering form. Gradually the killer draws ever closer to the unsuspecting rabbit, until, with a sudden bound, it is upon its victim, and we see the rabbit go down squealing with that high wail that is so piteous to hear.

Once a stoat gets rabbit it will follow rabbit seems to know is no escape, for crouch down and for mercy—which it and young game- this small, vicious I said I could tell of the black-tipped weasel, the other tiny about seven inches

YOUNG RABBITS

on the trail of a it for miles, and the that eventually there after a while it will cry and squeal as if does not get. Eggs birds also fall to killer. it was a stoat because tail, which the killer, lacks. Only long, the weasel is

much smaller than a stoat but similar in colour. It is so thin that it can follow a mouse down a hole. You would never think that such a tiny scrap of reddish fur could put such a fright into a rabbit, would you? But those wicked little teeth and those beady black eyes make up in quickness what the body lacks in size.

The more rabbits that are killed off the better, and it's a pity it is the close season now or I would show you how to set snares for these pests. They are very attractive to watch on a spring evening outside their burrows, I know, but they do millions of pounds' worth of damage each year by the quantity of green stuff they eat that should be eaten by us. Forty of them will eat as much as a dairy cow every day, and there are simply millions in every suitable piece of countryside. They multiply so quickly that it is only the fact that they have so many enemies to keep their numbers under control that the position does not become serious.

That reminds me of what happens when they are not disturbed. I was high on a desolate part of Salisbury Plain quite recently, and as no humans had been there for quite a long time it had become a happy breeding ground for rabbits, and never in my life have I seen so many youngsters. In every direction they were running around me, and as for Toby—well, words simply won't describe his emotions. He nearly went mad trying to catch a dozen at once, and after a while he was completely fagged; his tongue was hanging out in a limp pink strip, and his eyes were ringed with dirt. When we did reach a puddle in a muddy lane, he did not even stop to drink any, but threw himself down at full length in the muddy water, where he lay until he had recovered. What a day that was for him, but what a state the countryside would be in if rabbits were allowed to multiply everywhere like that!

Would you believe how the time has flown? It is almost lunch time, and I thought we should only be about two hours! Never mind! I think we'll call in at this snug-looking farmhouse and see if we can get a bite here. Usually I find lonely country farm folk only too willing to give me a simple meal and have a good gossip about things in general.

" We'm had a turr'ble bad toime we' foxes laitely," says Mrs. Grover, the farmer's better half, as she puts some tasty food and fresh milk before us. " Sumthin' shockun t'way moi chicks heve bin a'goin'."

" They must be the foxes we heard last night," you say at once; and I make a mental note to try to show you the vixen and her cubs at their rabbit-warren home, for they are such a wonderfully happy family.

" Goodbye, ma'am! " we say as we leave, carrying with us a bag of eggs and some milk.

" I'd like to live on a farm, wouldn't you, Woodman? " you say eagerly, as we walk back in the dusk, for we have had a good look round at the livestock first and the time soon passes.

" Well, it's a fine life, but there's never a moment when you haven't to be thinking of some job. I shouldn't like to be so tied to one place myself," I reply, as I fall to pondering the way I love to roam ever on fresh ground, and see fresh happenings in the world of the wild.

It is getting quite dark when we reach the caravan. The fire must be re-lit, preparations for supper made.

" Oh, yes! Sure you can try those dampers tonight," I tell you in answer to your eager query.

Out come the pots and pans ; once more we settle for the night, tired but happy.

There is always tomorrow.

CHAPTER III

Walks and Talks with Keeper Stokes

BIRD OCEAN-FLYERS—BIRDS AS WEATHER-PROPHETS—FRED STOKES, GAMEKEEPER—
THE FOX FAMILY AT HOME—YOU LEARN CALLS OF THE WILD—SUPPER AT THE
KEEPER'S COTTAGE

The afternoon is nicely warm.

Many miles have slipped by since we started our journey, and your notebook is becoming grimy and thumbed, but full of interesting little jottings, which you are getting down on all possible occasions.

We are sitting quietly by the caravan, sipping from our steaming tea mugs, when: " Cuckoo, cuckoo! " The two repeated notes break in sharply on the silence.

I fling back the call, imitating the two notes, and the slate-blue, hawk-like bird comes nearer. Right above the caravan he perches, shouting his monotonous call, while we watch silently.

Toby barks, and away flies the cuckoo, *the* bird of spring. Just as soon as he is heard in the country, windows are opened, coats are unbuttoned, and there is an air of " Well, it must be spring now " about the face of the countryside.

He's such a villain, too, and while we've been quietly watching the busy little hedgesparrow lining her dainty little mossy nest with a soft cushion of hairs, on which she will lay her sky-blue eggs, the cuckoo has also been watching the bird with an eye to business. And what a murderous business, to be sure!

Too lazy to make a nest of her own, the female cuckoo waits for a favourable moment, when the mother sparrow, tree-pipit or other small victim is away from the nest; then down she flies, takes out one of the rightful eggs, and lays one of her own in its place. She even adds a further insult by eating the stolen egg!

We can feel sorry for the poor, busy hedgesparrow, can't we? Soon after the eggs she will sit on so tightly hatch, the young cuckoo, blind and naked though he is, promptly commits murder by prising all the other youngsters out of the nest. There's no room for anyone else now he's about. Oh, no! When the foster-parent returns with a beakful of insects for the family, one wide gaping mouth takes the lot and yells for more!

After a few days the poor hardworking hedgesparrow wonders how on earth it ever hatched out such a huge, hungry, squalling off-spring, for the young cuckoo grows at a very fast rate and rapidly overflows the nest. As soon as he gets some downy feathers he perches on a nearby branch and yells for ever more food. Strangely enough, too, birds who should rightly be on their way to their own youngsters will often pause in their flight and push their beakful of insects into his ever-open mouth. So he grows, until I should think the pair of hedge-sparrows are thankful when at last he is able to fly off to forage for himself.

Then, in the autumn, occurs one of those amazing happenings that have puzzled for centuries the most clever of men. Untaught, and with nothing but a wonderful instinct to guide him, the young cuckoo will set out for the terrifically long journey across thousands of miles of the wastes of the great Atlantic, to spend the winter in a warmer land than ours. How does he know that he has to go, or how does he find the way? No one knows, but go he does, and just as certain as we are sitting here so back he will come next April, perhaps to the very spot where he was born.

" Whe-e-e-e, whe-e-e! "

Swish—and there flashing past us go a crowd of sooty-black swifts, which together with the swallows and martins, gayly soaring overhead, tell us in stronger words than the date on the calendar that spring is with us again.

" Can you tell the difference between swallows, swifts and martins, John?" I ask you. "You may be David, or Peter, or William, or Ian, but I'll just call you John for this trip. You won't mind, will you?"

TREE PIPIT FEEDING YOUNG CUCKOO

SWALLOWS UNDER THE EVES

"Well, Woodman, I think I know," you reply. "The swallows have those lovely forked tails, but the martins have only a small V in their tails, and a white patch on the back, which shows up pretty well just above the tail. The largest and swiftest fliers are the swifts. Their wings make such a lovely curve, like a bow, when they fly, don't they?"

Well, that's pretty good. The swift, too, is one of the most energetic birds you could ever meet, and never seems to rest. All this dashing about is not for fun, however, for, like the swallows and martins, the swifts feed as they fly, catching flies and insects in their wide-open, hair-lined mouths. The hairs slope backwards, so that insects cannot escape once they are trapped.

"Why do they sometimes all fly almost touching the ground, and at other times fly above the trees, Woodman?"

Well, birds and animals, as we shall probably see later on, are wonderful weather-prophets. When the air is heavy with rain, insects are forced down near the ground, and so the swallows nearly touch the ground as they skim over it. Then, on a fine spring evening, when the gnats are flying high in the light air, we can be certain of a fine day to come as we watch the birds catching their supper high above us.

"I think the most amazing thing is how the birds fly back over those vast distances against all weathers each spring to nest under the eaves of the same house where they were born, or in the same barn; don't you, Woodman?"

SWIFT

Yes, I do. Fancy tiny, featherweight birds like the swallow managing to survive all that journey! It certainly makes us think, doesn't it? Butterflies, too, although it is pretty hard to believe, also migrate, and they will fly across the Channel, and sometimes even cross the Atlantic with a following wind, resting on ships in clouds as they come. But we can't spend too much time gazing at the birds because I want to see if we can watch those fox-cubs this evening.

We are nearing the spot where I suspect the vixen has her cubs, when coming towards us I see a tall, lean man who walks as though he knows what he is about. He has huge pockets in his baggy coat, and carries a notched stick.

SWALLOW

He stops within a few feet of us, eyes us thoughtfully for a few moments from steely blue eyes that seem to see right through us, and then says slowly: " This is private land, sir. Can't have everyone coming through here disturbing the game birds, you know. Were you wanting anything here? "

He is looking now at Toby, who is safely on a lead, as he speaks, and something in Toby's expression seems to appeal to him, for he says, without waiting for a reply: " Intelligent-looking dog you have there. Bit of a collie in him, alongside plenty more, I shouldn't wonder."

I feel that things are not going to be difficult, for keepers are usually lovers of dogs, and, when you manage to get beneath their quiet, steady reserve with strangers, grand woodmen who really know what they are talking about when they speak, although they rarely waste words.

I answered his first question.

" I'm taking my young friend here to where I fancy we shall find a burrow full of fox-cubs. It's about half a mile over yonder. Maybe you know them?"

He nodded.

" You see, we are studying wild life, and, as a matter of fact, I was hoping to meet up with you. The good lady at the farm told us you would most probably be around here."

" Well, now, so you're after watching the foxes in Willow Tree corner, are you? Mebbe I'll take a stroll back there me'self, but you've to understand I can't allow just any Tom, Dick or Harry picnickers around here, sir. We get rare troubled with poachers here, being so near the main road."

SAND MARTINS

He falls in beside us, after giving Toby a pat. Hearing that you are John and want

GREEN WOODPECKER

so much to know about the countryside secrets, he begins to open out a bit to us, in response to your flood of questions.

"Do you try to kill all creatures apart from the partridges and pheasants?" you ask innocently.

"Lord 'a' mercy, no, young 'un!" cries the keeper, whose name, he tells us, is Fred Stokes. His tanned face wrinkles into a smile. "There's a good many birds that make me good sentries. I knew where you were long before I saw you. Did you notice how a cock blackbird dashed off when he saw your dog, screaming fit to bust, and how the wee wren was yelling his little head off to warn the others of your approach?"

You hadn't noticed these things, but I had, and so I had not been surprised when the keeper appeared.

"Maybe, though, the ol' starling gives me most fair warning, for he makes a rare to-do when he sights a sparrowhawk. If there's one varmint I like to get a bullet after it's a sparrowhawk: eggs go by the hundred where they're about."

Fred paused, and then continued:

"O' course, they're not t'only ones, by a long chalk. I simply can't abide a jay, with his egg-stealing, but he makes enough row to hear the other side of the wood when anyone comes near, and the ol' yaffle as we call the green woodpecker is another good 'un. Look, son, there's one now!"

He pointed to a greenish bird dashing off with a loping, up-and-down flight at our approach, making the evening air echo with its queer, mocking, ringing laugh.

"Yes, I get plenty of warning all right, but so will those foxes if we aren't careful."

We both knew that to catch the vixen napping, or any wild animal, for that matter, we had to come up-wind, that is with the breeze blowing *towards* us, and make no sound with snapping twigs underfoot. The fox knows how to make himself comfortable, and likes a dry bed. In this case the family had chosen a sheltered spot in a grassy hollow, where they had the benefit of the sun. They had taken over an unused rabbit warren, and had a solid home.

We creep nearer the spot, watching for the first move from the bird sentinels that would betray us; but luck is on our side, and at long last we reach the edge of the hollow and peer over. There below us is a sight that makes our Red-Indian movements well worth while, for rolling, yapping and fighting, for all the world like five woolly puppies, are the cubs, watched over by the fox and vixen for the first signs of danger.

They are as fond of games as kittens, are these cubs, but even at a very early age they have wonderfully sharp senses, particularly the sense of smell.

For the first month the mother feeds them entirely on her own milk, but they are very quick pupils, and she soon shows them how to prepare for a very hard life by teaching them how to catch rats and young rabbits, which Fred doesn't mind in the least, and, later, young pheasants and partridges, which certainly does upset him!

There are very few parents who are more devoted than the fox family, and even Fred agrees with this, but, by gosh, how he wants to see the " varmint " out of the way before his young game stock is hatched out!

Suddenly your foot slips. It couldn't be helped, but it is enough to send the whole family off like a shot.

" They're the very dickens to trap; cunning just ain't the word for 'em," Fred says, as we walk back towards his cottage, for you have insisted that we go back to see his vermin pole, and, as he puts it,

THE FOX FAMILY

" The missus 'll be glad to give you a bite. It's rare we have strangers for a chat."

Thus honoured at being invited to his lonely cottage, we walk through the gathering gloom of the wood, for it soon becomes quite dark among the trees.

" Can you call birds and animals so they come to you? " you ask Fred, after we have trudged a way in silence.

"That I can, and many a time I've found it useful," the keeper says. " You take a rabbit, now. If you want to get him out of his burrow just you try putting your lips at the back of your hand and draw in your breath hard. Try it now with me."

You do as he says, and at first produce a few squeaky noises, but soon you get a bit better, and after Fred had shown you how it really should be done, making a noise just like the squealing of a rabbit badly frightened, you are determined to keep on practising tomorrow.

" Rabbits 'll come to see what the noise is about, partly because of fear and partly because they're just plain curious. There's a good, old, true saying, you know, ' curiosity killed the cat ', and I reckon it often fits rabbits."

He chuckles and winks at me, then continues: " Mark you, the rabbit is no coward when it comes to protecting her young. I suppose there's nothing she fears so much as a weasel or a stoat, yet I've known an old doe with a litter attack and kick a stoat so hard that he was glad to run off with his tail between his legs. That took a bit of courage, you know."

" Coo, I should have liked to see *that!* " you exclaim admiringly. " I'd never have thought the rabbit had it in her."

" Neither did the stoat, I'm thinking," the keeper chuckles. " Now watch me, and I'll show you how to call the brown owl," he continues, after a pause.

STOAT

LEVERET

He places his hands together, puts his lips to the top knuckles of his thumb, and blows into the hollow of his hands through his thumbs, so that a beautiful liquid blast, like a deep flute, is heard. Imitating the long and short notes of the bird's long, trembling cry exactly, in a few moments he has the wood ringing with answering cries from brown owls on the search for their supper.

When this noise has died down a bit, Fred, warming up to his subject, adds: " Take the hare, now. There ain't many another animal as hard to get near as that long-legged, lonely critter, but if you're smart you can, with a bit of luck, attract him near you. You just get a bit of stick, about a couple of feet long, stick it to the ground in the middle of an open field, and put a turnip or two, or a few carrots, near by." As an afterthought, he added: " There ain't nothing hares are so fond of as carrots, unless it be carnations, and they're real critters for them! "

Pausing just long enough to chuckle over this, he carries on: " The hare will come pottering around near the stick, especially when there is snow about, and you'll get a real good chance to study his tracks. If you do see a stick a-standing by itself like I said, just you watch out for traps set around—and just a little point to remember: hares love a meadow where there's plenty of sheep's parsley best."

" Hares live wild, solitary lives, don't they? " I say, as we near Fred's cottage. " It seems as if nature really meant the poor old hare to be always ready for trouble, for it's next to impossible to be in the same field without its getting to know. This business about being mad as a March hare, too. Well, I reckon that the creature deserves a *little* pleasure sometimes, and the windy nights of March are the only times of the year when some strange urge for company seizes whole groups of hares, drawing them together for midnight revels in some sheltered field. Then they become for a short time as ' mad as hatters ', and take this chance to pair up. Just as suddenly as they came together, though, they will all be gone one night, back to their lonely life."

"The young hares are called leverets, aren't they?" you exclaim. "And they don't burrow like rabbits, do they, but live in 'forms' in the open? Why is that, Woodman?"

"Perhaps Fred will tell you," I reply, and that worthy takes up the story willingly.

"Well, it's like this see, son. Rabbits live together for protection, and when one scents or spots trouble he signals the alarm by thumping the ground hard with his back legs, and the whole lot scatter to the warrens quick as light. But with the hare it's different. They don't even seem to get on well with the rabbits, and having their home above ground they are always able to watch for danger, and, believe me, a hare can spot anything moving for a long way off when it sits upon its long back legs. Its sandy coat seems to merge well into the ground, too, and it's mighty difficult to shoot because it will zig-zag across a field like a streak, doubling back on its own tracks to put a dog off the scent."

The conversation would have gone on like this for some time, for Fred didn't often have interested company, but at this moment through a clearing in the trees we come upon his cottage, a well-cared-for, solidly thatched little building, from the parlour window of which a welcome yellow light is shining, showing up the pattern of the latticed frames.

"You there, Ma?" Fred calls as we enter the parlour. "Got company with me. They'll be staying awhile, I guess."

So saying, he pulls up two extra chairs to the fire, and, with the cheerful Mrs. Stokes busy in the background like a fussy hen, the drowsy warmth of the fire, and the general feeling of well-being, I feel almost too sleepy to want to move again this night—and, by the looks of you, you are feeling the same.

Night always seems to catch up with us so soon, doesn't it, John?

CHAPTER IV

Invaders in the Woods

A DAY WITH THE KEEPER—GAME-BIRDS AND THEIR WAYS—HOW TO TELL WILD BIRDS—
THE JAY GIVES THE ALARM—THE NUTHATCH PLASTERER—HOW NOT TO GET LOST IN
WOODS—A WATCH AS COMPASS

"I simply couldn't eat another thing, really, Mrs. Stokes!" I have to exclaim at the end of one of the tastiest suppers we have had since we started our trip.

We push our plates away, get out pipes, and resettle round the fire. The clock on the mantelshelf ticks away the minutes and then the hours, until I have to say:

"Well, John, old scout. We'll simply have to go now. There's another day ahead tomorrow."

Turning to Fred I add: "I don't know if you find it so, but the days seem to flash by when you're out all day. We've been on the road now for nearly three weeks and it doesn't seem like three days."

"I don't know how those poor office chaps stick it, being shut up all year," replies the keeper. "Fair missing most of their life! But wait a minute; you've got a rare long walk back to that caravan of yours. Why not spend the night here along with us, if you don't mind roughing it a bit? If you're not in a hurry I could show young John here a few mighty interesting things tomorrow."

We look at each other, and you say excitedly: "Can we stay, Woodman? I'd love to."

"Well, keeper, I don't want to put you out, you know . . ." I begin, but Mrs. Stokes cuts me short, and eventually we bed down comfortably in the spare bedroom between sheets giving off a variety of different inviting, clean smells, such as you only get in the country where visitors are rare.

The hours tick by.

Cock-crow! The barn owl's last trembling call before sleep, the cheerful, happy "go-to-it" of the song-thrush, and the eastern sky is pale yellow once more. The world of the great outdoors stirs for another day.

Down below, Fred and his stout-hearted helpmate are stirring.

"Come on, John, lad; show a leg! By the looks of that sky we're in for another great day."

We tumble out of bed, dress quickly, for it is very cold in the early morning in spring, and descend the creaking, narrow staircase.

"How d'you sleep?" Fred greets us, while his wife hands us two huge steaming cups of tea.

We tell him we've slept like logs, and over a hearty breakfast he tells us of his plans for the day.

The sun, rising rapidly, helps to dispel the heavy ground mist, and when we start out the air is beautifully clear, and smells of mingled damp earth and pines greet us.

We breathe in deeply, and Fred says: "Some people come charging about on land like this like a herd of elephants. Takes me all my time trying to keep 'em away from my game. They don't seem to realise that partridges and pheasants be sitting hard now, and a badly frightened bird, as like as not, will desert her eggs."

This is, we can see, a sore point with him, and you ask: "Tell me a bit about their habits, Mr. Stokes, will you please?"

"Well, young 'un, pheasants are early layers, and by mid-April the birds are usually sitting. Partridges are a bit later, and although some of them begin to lay about the end of April they are mostly the French sort, or red-legs, as we call them. Most partridges begin to lay about the end of the first week in May, and start sitting tight about the end of the month."

"By Midsummer Day you usually reckon to have the majority hatched off, don't you?" I break in.

"That's right; so you can see the pheasant has a longer nesting-time than the partridge, and I shall be finding them sitting until the end of June now."

We approach a patch of bracken, and Fred says, "Now, I'll show you a nest, and see if you can spot the bird sitting."

He points to a spot, but strain our eyes as we might we cannot see anything unusual, until suddenly there is a terrific "whirr" and the hen pheasant flies off. She has kept still as long as she is able, but the sight of Toby proves too much for her in the end.

We would never have seen the fifteen olive eggs in their warm, soft, lined nest if she had not flown off, so well had she blended in with the bracken.

PHEASANTS

" I can't stand crowds who come breaking down the hedges after primroses and bluebells," Fred says. " They're the ones who do most damage, for the birds prefer to nest in these openish places." He goes on to tell us how dangerous and cruel it is to trespass on the land he sets aside for chick-rearing, which is one of his most important spring jobs. The stranger who ventures near the coops, with their very attractive, speckled, fluffy youngsters, absolutely terrifies the birds, and in their fright they rush headlong to the wrong coops and are pecked to death by jealous foster-mothers. Many others, crouching in the undergrowth, are trod on and crushed, for one of the most difficult things to spot is a squatting young pheasant or partridge, for when in the open they will scatter at a warning call from their parents and are invisible at once.

Fred says they get used to his everyday clothes and leggings, though, and take no notice of him, but if he was to come down to look at them in his Sunday best, then he would probably lose half of them.

Soon after midsummer he will take the young birds he has so carefully shielded from fox, stoat, owl and hawk, and turn them loose in the coverts, where they will remain until they are flushed to make a target for some rich man's gun in the autumn shoots. Should strangers pass through these coverts in the late evening after the birds, having learned to fly, roost in the low branches of trees or on the stems of the undergrowth, the birds will fly from the roosts in whirring crowds and will spend the night on the ground, where they fall an easy victim to the fox.

" Ah, just you let me catch anyone through here then ! " Fred says, with a wealth of meaning in his words. " They'll go out quicker'n they came in."

Suddenly on the ground in front of us you almost tread on a squat little object that looks like a frog. You pick it up, and say to the keeper: " What young bird is this, Mr. Stokes? "

" Give a guess, son," Fred replies, and as you gaze at the drab-brown little bird, spotted with bright yellow, you try to place it, but somehow you just cannot.

PIGEONS

" Well, it's a young robin, although I know he doesn't look much like one at the moment," Fred says, after you have had several tries. " You see, it is useful for him to look like a frog and so get passed over by his enemies, and it is not until the autumn, when he is able to take care of himself, that he gets the bright red breast we are so fond of."

As we walk through the springy undergrowth towards the river that flows at the bottom of the long wood, he goes on to explain that a young cuckoo in the nest will often resemble a snake, for with his long neck extended over the edge of the nest that is just what he looks like.

Of course, other birds look like their parents as soon as their ugly, naked little bodies are covered with the first downy feathers. Sparrows are very much like the mother bird for some time after they have tried their wings, but the youngsters have very yellowish corners to their mouths, and this is a good way of quickly telling a young bird. Wobbly flying and the way they make a scrambling grab at a branch to perch are other signs. All youngsters also keep up a steady *cheep* as they follow their parents about.

If you discover a nest full of blackbirds, you will probably think they are all hens, for they all have the mother's brownness, dotted with muddy-brown spots, and their beaks, like the mother's, are dull, and so unlike the brilliant orange of the cock bird, who, too, has a rich, velvety black coat.

Young thrushes look like their brown parents from the first, and have the same attractive almost white breast, with rows of brown spots.

"Here, wait a minute! I think we can see some young thrushes right now," I say, as I suddenly hear a loud cheeping in a nearby bush, and, sure enough, in a strongly made nest of grasses, lined very solidly with a smooth mud coating, are five youngsters. The first thing we see is the bright yellow of the insides of their gaping throats, and this colour is usual, except in the crow-tribe, where the young birds' throats are very bright flesh-colour.

Bits of hair and the thrush's saliva are mixed with mud to make the wonderfully strong lining she gives the nest, and its smoothness is obtained by the bird turning round and round, using her breast as a trowel.

Young starlings are dull in drab-brown feathers, but they have the fine speckling of the old birds.

Pointing suddenly upward towards two swiftly disappearing grey birds, Fred says: "Young wood-pigeons! I wonder if you could see that they had no white ring round their necks? It's autumn before they get this, and it's even later before their toes change from dull pinkish to the bright red of the brown birds. The young 'uns have slate-coloured beaks, too, but they change to orange in autumn."

"What's the first thing you usually notice about wood-pigeons as they fly, John?" I ask you.

"The white bars across the wings, and also the way they clap their wings together over their heads with a sharp crack when they are startled," you reply, feeling quite proud of having noticed this trick of the wood-pigeon, which often tells the keeper where there are poachers.

"You can easily pick out a young partridge," Fred explains, "by its all-over-alike drabness, but later on it's more difficult. The young 'un will have a yellowish leg, however."

The conversation has been drifting on quietly as we walk, but suddenly we are startled by a screeching, squawking cry, something like someone tearing a strip of strong calico from top to bottom! It is the cry of the most wideawake bird of the woods, and the most handsome, the jay.

"It 'ud take a mighty clever man to get near him without his knowing," Fred says, with a chuckle. "Regular helpmate to me when there's strangers about. He's a real handsome villain, with black beak, grey-black crest, and bright blue and jet-black bars on the small wing-feathers. He's also got lovely chestnut wings, black tail, and strawberry-coloured chest and back. Ah, he's a real gay fellow, but a rare egg stealer!"

" He's about the most cunning and wary creature of the woods, isn't he, keeper? " I comment.

" Aye, and the most inquisitive; but he's the first to spread the alarm at the sight of a stoat, cat, dog, or poacher," Fred says. " One of the strongest of the birds of this wood, I reckon," he continues. " All his strength seems centred in his beak, as with all the crow-like birds, if you notice. It 'ud be more'n you could do to pull your finger away from a jay's nip. His beak is like a pair of strong scissors, and, by gosh, they can hold. He feeds on grubs, insects, young birds, eggs and corn. Of course, I don't mind how many wood-pigeons he robs; the more of their white eggs he takes the better—and, speaking of eggs, I reckon if you're good at climbing, young 'un, you can see some of the jay's eggs yourself now."

So saying, he points to a fairly thick nest of twigs placed cunningly at the slender top of a birch pole, where it seems impossible to reach them. But near by is a solid-looking tree-trunk, and by climbing this you are able to gaze down at the neat, root-lined cup of the nest, and see the five bluish-green eggs, speckled with dark spots, like those of a blackbird.

As usual, the jay has shown himself to be a cunning homemaker, for he does not lay himself open to attack from stoat or weasel as does the dove and wood-pigeon, who build their slender twig nests in more solid trees, as a rule. Birch poles are mighty difficult to climb, even for an animal like the weasel.

The young birds seem to understand the need for silence as long as they remain in the nest, and it is not until they begin to fly about that they make the wood resound with their chatter.

" What's that queer little bird running up that trunk? " you exclaim, after you have dusted yourself down, and we have resumed our stroll.

We look to where you indicate, and see a well-built stocky bird, with a strong, short tail, slate-grey head and back, and a pinkish-buff waist-coat. He has a saucy-looking black line running through his eye, and carries a blob of mud in his strong beak.

" That's a nuthatch," I reply. " Just you watch how his stiff tail helps him in climbing up the trunk."

We watch him, keeping quite quiet and still, and see him reach a small hole, which is already liberally plastered with mud.

" He's a rare clever little 'un, the way he makes his nesting hole just the size to suit him," Fred says in admiration. " If you fix a few

NUTHATCH nuts in a tree-trunk in the garden in winter you may be lucky enough to watch him then."

We have swung round in our walk and are heading back to the cottage, when Fred says: "Do you know how to stop yourself getting lost in a wood, John?"

You shake your head, for it has always been a source of admiration to you how a man like Fred never seems to lose his bearing.

"Well, when you enter a wood, notice on which cheek the wind blows, or how it blows the tree-tops; so as long as the wind holds that way you shouldn't lose your way. Make a point of constantly looking behind you as you go too, because you'll find that the way back always looks altogether different. Try to remember any dead trees or other outstanding signs, so that they will help you to keep to the same track back."

I remove my wrist-watch as Fred finishes, and add to his remarks.

"If you have a watch, John, you can find north and south with it, if the sun is shining. Point the hour hand to the sun, and lay a thin twig along the watch-face midway between the hour hand and twelve on the watch. The twig will then be pointing north and south. But, as you usually haven't a watch, or it is dull, you had better remember the tips Mr. Stokes has given you."

You spend the rest of the walk back to the cottage continually looking back and memorising little things, and by the time we see the caravan once more, after bidding farewell to Fred, whose wife tells us that we must come again in the autumn, we are tired once more.

Tomorrow we start on the trail back homewards. Holidays go so quickly, but soon we start another trip, for the spring and summer months are all too short, and the summer journey should be worth waiting a little time for.

Meanwhile, we will spend our weekends tramping together, ever adding to your notes, shall we?

Dawn again! We turn Robby to the road back, the caravan creaks, and the harness jangles pleasantly. It begins to rain, beating with hearty thumps on the roof. We whistle, and sing a few tramping songs. Sometimes even in spring we must have rain.

CHAPTER V

The Shepherd of the Hills

SUMMER IN THE CLOCKLESS OPEN-AIR—ON THE SHEEP-DOWNS—THE SHEPHERD AND
HIS DOG—LIFE IN THE SOLITUDES—TRICKING THE CORNCRAKE—NIGHTJARS AND
NIGHTINGALES—"SUGARING" FOR MOTHS—THE HUNTER HAWKS

Where the hedges were black such a short time ago, they now have a coat of vivid green. Evenings that were early dusk on our spring journey are now light, until my clock tells me it is time to turn in for the night.

"Tick, tick, tick," with never a pause, the hands revolve on his face. It is time to get up; it is time to work; it is time to go to bed. He is a dictator, isn't he? The trees are bare; they are rich green; brown leaves flutter to the ground; snow covers everything; still he ticks away solemnly.

Those whose lives are spent in the open, however, have no need of his steady ticking to know what time of day it is. As the pale light of dawn stirs the lark and the thrush, so, too, do open-air folk rise, make their strong tea, and start on their daily round. They glance at the sun and know when it is time for their sandwiches and their bottle of cold tea. Just as the cows know when to plod slowly down to the gate, patiently to await the milker, so the man who works in the open knows when to down tools and trudge home to the steaming kettle in his cottage. Just as the rooks fly back to the elms to roost at the approach of night, so he climbs the "wooden hill" to bed.

"Afternoon, sir! We'm a-wantin' some rain rare bad."

The man who lives in the lonely places, Bill Speak, the shepherd, gives us the greeting as we near his flock on this lovely early-summer afternoon.

As we had climbed the downs we spotted him, standing there quiet and still as a stone, a perfect picture. The sheep-bells jingle softly;

Bill leans on his staff and gazes down at us. Rover sits at his side, his keen eyes watching our every move.

" My word, that's a stiff climb today! " you exclaim as we pantingly reach the shepherd. " I'm jolly glad we brought some drink."

From our rucksack we take sandwiches and drink, and as we munch our meal we gaze across the miles of open patchwork quilt that stretches away into the bluey distance.

I offer Bill a plug of tobacco for his blackened old pipe. He puffs away contentedly at this, and we feel some of his steady enjoyment of life as we sit here, while from away below come the sounds of the village.

" Ah, but t'aint allus as quiet as this, y'know," Bill says after a long silence. " Come they January lambs, and you, sir, and nor you, young 'un, 'ould find it such a picnic up here. There ain't much rest day nor night while that's a-going on."

He tells us how he builds the straw-and-hurdle shelters to protect the newly born lambs from the bitter winds, of the way he looks forward with eagerness to the twins in the flock, and that many is the time he has not had his boots off for days or perhaps weeks at a stretch. What he does not tell us is the love and devotion with which he watches over the flock at this time, ready at all hours of the cold, black nights to help with the birth of yet another youngster, born in the flickering light of his lamp. The flock know him, and he, for his part, devotes the whole of his hours to their welfare. His hut-on-wheels, a little black shelter that he has to call " home " for many a day, sees him but little at this time, and if it were not for the ever-faithful companionship of Rover he would not speak to a friend, unless it was on the occasions when the farmer visits him to find out how things are going.

Bill says Rover means more to him than any human. " He's a rare clever 'un. Might as well be without my right arm as Rover," he exclaims, and at this Rover cocks his ears, and looks at his master with soft, lovely brown eyes. His tail hits the grass once or twice, and then he turns his head to resume his watchful gaze over the flock.

Bill's face and hands show traces, in the mass of deep wrinkles and knobbly knuckles, of the hard toil of his life, for just as the year changes, so does his daily round, and there is forever some fresh task for his skilled fingers. He knows, too, all the ways of the wilds, and can cunningly snare any animal he wants, and point out all the nesting partridges within his area.

" Have you a crook, shepherd? " you ask, and at this Bill smiles, for his handy staff is not shaped like the many paintings you have seen, but has a narrow eye to enable him to catch sheep by its hind legs for examination, marking, trimming or shearing.

In early spring he moves his sheep daily to new portions of the fields of kale. Bill, as stout of heart as ever he was, is beginning to feel the strain of the work more each year, and as we sit together on this warm afternoon, when he can bask in the sun, I wonder who will take his place when he is gone.

Ah, John, I am afraid Bill, like our friend the keeper, belongs to a dying race. There are ever fewer to take their place in the solitary life of the wilds.

Suddenly Rover is off like a streak to the scene of some disturbance on the edge of the flock. At his bark Bill gets up and we hurry over. One of the sheep is on its side, kicking furiously, and trying vainly to regain its legs.

" See that now? " says Bill. " A sheep that slips over somehow 'll die unless it is put on its feet again. That's one of the little things I have to watch." So saying, he heaves the sheep to its feet, and with a run it is away and into the flock.

" Well, Bill, we'll be getting back now," I say as the shadows start to lengthen from the clump of elms, which he uses as a sundial. " We've a good walk ahead."

We wave him goodbye, and Rover sends us off with a cheerful bark. A white mist is beginning to form near the ground, for the air soon becomes damp and chilly in the evenings in early summer.

As we walk through the grass, there is a constant " crak, crak, crak ", seeming to come from all parts at once.

" What's that? " you ask.

" One of the birds you will very, very rarely see, although he makes such a row, John—a corn-crake. He comes to visit us from Egypt, but when he does get here he spends all his time

running about in the corn, and you
can see how he got his name. He
is not very common now."

I feel in my pocket and take out
two bones, each notched along one
edge.

"I'm going to see if I can't
attract him over to us, John, by
using these 'crake-bones'. They give a pretty
fair imitation of his cry when I drag them
against each other."

So saying, we squat down near the hedge,
whilst I " crake " with the bones.

The bird replies, coming closer all the
time. Suddenly he appears right in front of us, but directly he spots
us he turns on his long legs and runs like a hare.

" Well, John, that's the last we shall see of the corncrake, but whilst
we are here I think we might try to catch a closer glimpse of another
queer bird of the evening. Can you hear that long ' chur-r-r ', like an
old-time night-watchman's rattle, coming from that bird over there? "

You nod, watching whilst a dark shape flits by calling " co-ick, co-ick "
as it passes.

" That's the nightjar, John. It comes out in the evening in search
of moths and other insects, just the same as the bats. It is one of those
birds that seem exactly to match the undergrowth when at rest, and that's
a good thing, because it lays its eggs on the ground, quite without any
covering. They are pretty difficult to see, though."

There is a sharp " crack " as the nightjar slaps its wings together over
its back, and the noise sounds very magnified in the dusk.

While we have been keeping still in the hedge-bottom, a turtle-dove
has settled above, and its quickly repeated, purring " coo", sounding
just like " tur, tur, tur, tur ", is wonderfully soothing. Another sound
that seems to come from all around us is the " cri, cri, cri-cri-cri " of the
grasshopper, rubbing his back legs together briskly over his back. They
move at an amazing speed, these legs, and produce his cheerful little
song. He has big eyes, has friend grasshopper, and well he needs them,
for even though he has a green coat to protect him he is snapped up by
kestrel-hawk, sparrow and other birds as a dainty titbit, if he shows himself too well.

The field-crickets are adding to the general orchestra, too, rubbing their wings one upon the other, and altogether there is quite a medley as we walk through the quickly dampening grass.

"My word, there are some large moths about this evening!" you exclaim as we pass a patch of highly scented honeysuckle, giving out an even greater perfume now that it is evening, in order to attract the moth. "Some of my friends at school have good collections of moths. Do you think you could show me how to catch them by 'sugaring', as they call it, Woodman?"

"Yes, John, I will later on, for I think the autumn is best. I well remember how I caught hundreds in one night by sugaring. I mixed up some treacle with a drop of beer, to give it a smell, and added a little methylated spirits, just to make the moths drunk, you know. Then I roughly painted this mess round a tree-trunk and settled down with a hurricane lamp and a white sheet behind it. Well, what with one attraction and another, I was kept busy gathering in a fine batch of moths, some of which, like the lovely hawk-moth, were real beauties. The frogs and toads round about had a good night, too, for they gathered round to catch any moths that fell off the sticky sugar. Yes, it's good fun, John, and

SMALL TORTOISE SHELL

DEATH'S-HEAD HAWK-MOTH

when we go we may see several other night-lovers too, for a light always seems to attract any creature."

"I'll have to get a good net made," you say, and just to test your knowledge I ask, "Do you know the difference between butterflies and moths, John?"

"Well, I know that the moths have thick, furry-looking bodies, and that their 'feelers' haven't any knobs on the end, as butterflies have. Moths come out in the evening, too, when the butterflies are going to bed."

"Yes, that's right, and do you remember the first butterflies we saw this spring? They were rather worn-looking tortoiseshells and those lovely yellow brimstones, weren't they?—all old-stagers who had spent the winter asleep in the crevice of some tree-trunk or among the rafters of a barn. It's rather wonderful how they manage to survive our very hard winter, isn't it?"

FIELD CRICKET

"I always think the most marvellous part about a butterfly or a moth is the way the caterpillar changes into that dead-looking case—chrysalis, isn't it, Woodman?—and then after a while breaks out into such a lovely object. All that powder on the wings that brushes off when we touch a butterfly enables it to fly, doesn't it?"

"Yes, and if we could look at the wings under a microscope we should see countless little scales all overlapping and enabling the butterfly to 'take-off'. They have a very good sense of smell, and those wretched cabbage whites, which lay their eggs underneath cabbage-leaves, producing those green caterpillars that strip the plants, leaving just the skeletons, are attracted by the definite smell of the leaves. As soon as the caterpillars hatch from the yellow eggs, they eat and eat until they burst their skins, and as soon as the new skin is dry they start again. You can see how easily a number will strip all the leaves from a cabbage patch, and the pity is that birds dislike them, otherwise their numbers would be kept down."

"What happens to the caterpillar then, Woodman?"

"Well, eventually it stops eating and fixes itself to some object by a

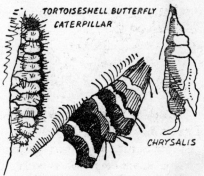

TORTOISESHELL BUTTERFLY CATERPILLAR

CHRYSALIS

HIBERNATING IN WINTER. IN BARN

silk thread, which comes from a tube just under its mouth, and its body gradually turns into a chrysalis, which dries into a hard shell. Now it seems to go to sleep for a while, and during this time the green caterpillar turns into a handsome butterfly. After about two or three weeks

KESTREL

the chrysalis splits open, and the butterfly, with damp, limp wings, comes out. It's a really wonderful change altogether. But we'll talk more about them when we go ' mothing ', for at the moment I want to watch that kestrel-hawk over there! "

So saying, we pause by a tree-trunk, and watch a dark shape hovering high above us in a nearby field. With just an occasional flutter of his wings and tail, the kestrel hangs as though suspended from a piece of string, while his keen eyes search the ground below for mice and other scurrying creatures. Suddenly he spots a movement, shuts his wings, and drops like a stone, flying up from a grassy clump a moment later with a mouse clutched tightly in his steel-like claws.

Away he goes, flying off with food for the family, which will be housed in the old home of a magpie or crow, or sometimes on a cliff ledge.

We near the coppice through which we always walk on the way home, and I notice a small pile of green feathers strewn beneath one of the hazels.

" Ah! It looks as if the sparrow-hawk has been hunting here, John," I exclaim, for we know that in one of the tall pine-trees is a large, shallow nest containing the fluffy young hawks.

The sparrow-hawk is very different in habits from the kestrel, as we have noticed many times in our walks. He likes to keep very much under cover, and his favourite hunting trick is to glide rapidly down one side of a hedge, suddenly dart over the top, and dash among a crowd of small birds peacefully feeding on the other side. Before they have time to get over their fright, he has seized a victim, and once caught in those long claws there is no escape. Both the parents are pale-buff underneath, closely barred with brown, and when standing at the nest they appear to be wearing trousers half-way down their yellow legs. They are very fierce fighters and will not hesitate to attack even a bird larger than themselves.

This coppice is a happy hunting ground for us, for it is just large enough to contain a good variety of wild life, and I want to see this evening if we can spot that marvellous little songster, the nightingale. We have heard him several times, but have not yet caught sight of him.

It is rather still in the coppice, as it always is in a wood, for birds and beasts seem to prefer the outskirts, and you will find much more to study there, as a rule.

As we walk, I give four slow, long-drawn whistles, and although they cannot be said to imitate the little russet-coated singer's notes they are sufficient to make him take up the challenge. He breaks the silence of the wood with his liquid notes, and we stand and listen, too thrilled to go further until we have heard his full range. On and on he goes, however, and eventually we manage to stalk him by his song, until we can just catch a glimpse of him, perched on a hazel bough and thoroughly enjoying himself.

"Where does the nightingale come from, Woodman? He isn't here all the winter, is he?" you ask, as we leave the spot, knowing that safely hidden in a cosy nest near the ground the hen bird, who can only utter a few call notes, is hatching out her eggs.

"Well, like so many small birds we welcome each year, John, he comes from a winter in Africa. At the beginning of March he commences his long journey of over three thousand miles, getting here about mid-April. When they do arrive, however, a pair

NIGHTINGALE

are quite ready to spend all their time with us in one small coppice, like this one, and their little world consists of about an acre. Our little singer gets here about ten days before his more sober and quiet wife, and it is during this time that fierce fights between rival males over a desired piece of land take place, and just as with two rival robins the victor shouts in triumph from the hedge-tops and remains the proud possessor of his chosen spot. When the hens do arrive, the cock birds really get going with their singing, and they will show off before the hens. It is a fine sight, John, and I should have liked you to see it this year. Proud as a peacock, the cock will alight on a branch near the hen, hold his long russet tail over his back, raise and lower his wings, and try to show himself off in all his glory. He does all this slowly and perfectly, and sometimes he flies off and returns quickly with a beakful of food for the hen, which she takes quite readily."

I have been talking quite softly, but my voice is loud enough to disturb a tiny little brown bird, who flits to a nearby branch and scolds us in ringing tones, which would do credit to a bird many times its size.

"Jenny *is* annoyed!" you say as we walk past the wren's nesting site, and to show that you are right the scolding chatter follows us for quite a way farther.

In a hole in a decayed tree-trunk, hidden by tiny leaves, Jenny Wren has her beautifully cosy mossy home, with a small entrance-hole in the side to admit her plump little body. She lays a large clutch of tiny, almost transparent, white, brown-spotted eggs, and a pair of wrens kill off many thousands of insects when they are feeding their family. I remember how, in the walled garden of a French farm which I visited daily for delicious home-baked bread, Jenny Wren was a very welcome little guest, and her mossy home was protected by the family against cats and other foes. That garden contained more nests than I have ever found in the same space in this country, and even though those walls may have been blasted down now I feel sure the wrens will still be building in the ruins.

We are silent as we near the cottage where Mother is waiting with a good supper for both of us. We are both thinking of the packing we must do, for tomorrow we start off on another caravan tour. You are not sorry that you have an unexpected holiday, I am sure. No, the life of the open road has gripped you as it forever grips me.

CHAPTER VI

Camouflage in the Bird World

MAY ON THE MARSHLAND—ANGRY WHITE SPIRITS—THE WILD BEAUTY OF THE
LONELY PLACES—DANGER OF THE "MARSH GAS"—HOW BIRDS HIDE FROM ENEMIES

From the cliff top, the marshland stretches below us like some shimmering, lonely land that is part of another world. It is May, and the whole marsh, covered with marren grass and bright with patches of sea pinks, is alive with countless flashing wings. Here we are right in the heart of a haunt of the black-headed gull, which has known and nested in this lonely yet strangely luring spot for many years.

The marsh is crossed and recrossed by countless riverlets and channels, the black mud of which sucks viciously at the water that ebbs quickly into the broad silver of the river leading to the sea. Red-shanks, dunlin, snipe, and many other waders run at the edge of the receding water, picking up the various small water-shrimps and shell-fish left in the mud, and over all there is an air of wildness such as we have never yet felt as we trundled along the dusty country lanes.

" I love the marshland, Woodman! " comes the exclamation I have expected. " It all seems so exciting, and, my word, don't those gulls seem in a rage about our being here! "

Yes, the gulls certainly are in a rage, and are showing their anger in no uncertain manner. Down they swoop in endless procession, tearing at our heads, and only braking with an angry, frustrated " krrk " when they are within a few inches. The alarm had been given when we were still a good way from the colony by the sentinel gulls, flying high and away from the main body.

" Tek, tek, tek," came the warning cries as they spotted our small boat, and within a few moments the marshland, which had looked quite deserted when first we viewed it from far off, became alive with countless flashing white wings, until now the air seems to have become filled with angry white spirits, all intent on keeping us away from their nests. Their laugh-like screams rose to a still higher pitch as I moored our craft and you, John, jumped on to the coarse grass by the side of one of the salty pools which dot the marsh as legacies of the receding tide.

Our voices become lost in the general babel, and both of us feel in the grip of a strange excitement. The marsh seems so huge, and we both feel so small and almost at the mercy of those thousands of angry gulls, who are treating us like the intruders we are! Grey-green-backed crabs scuttle into the mud of the pools as we approach, making an opaque patch where they disappeared, whilst almost transparent shrimps jump like jumping-beans wherever there is a free patch of mud.

But the nests of the gulls are what attract our attention most, for a.l around the pools they spread, clustered in groups of two or three together. Grass, sedges, rushes, seaweed and other weeds, thrown together to make an untidy cup, hold the two or three eggs, and these vary in colour to an enormous extent. Although we examine hundreds, never two do we find exactly to match. Greenish-grey-brown or olive is the general main colour, while splashes, mottles, and zig-zag markings of every shape add to their variety and beauty.

" Look over there, John," I say, as I spot two of what I feel sure are some of the prettiest of all newly hatched birds. " Don't they make you think of young ducklings ? "

Sure enough, in general appearance, the youngsters, gay, delightful balls of buff down striped with black and brown, with big feet and bright eyes, do look like perky little ducks. Into the water they dive as we approach them, for although their down is only just dry from the egg still they are able to swim, and have the instinct of self-protection strong with them. Like young chicks and ducklings, however, this delightful " Easter-egg " appearance soon goes, and later they will become brown-marked; until they are in their first winter they will have little white about them.

" Gosh, Woodman, I feel I'd like to take some of these home," you say, with an enthusiasm which makes me think vividly of the first time I saw these gay little youngsters, so very different from the helpless, skinny, naked and thoroughly unattractive creatures that we see at a few days old in the nests of thrush, blackbird and other hedgerow birds.

It is an amazing thing how each bird is born admirably suited to its surroundings and fitted to begin a struggle for life that is never-ending. Some birds use camouflage to a remarkable extent to hide from their many enemies, and we found that out with a vengeance when we tried to stalk a partridge family. The ever-watchful parents, themselves a drab-brownish shade that seemed to blend in well with their surroundings in the undergrowth, soon spotted us, although we were keeping quite still, and within a few seconds of the alarm cry being given it was impossible to find one of the twelve tiny balls of brownish fluff, although we knew that they were within a few feet of us. Off like streaks in all directions they had gone, diving into the first clump of grass that would hide their wee bodies—and a leaf would suffice at that age, for they were only a few days old—and with fast-beating hearts they would remain until we had gone from the scene, never moving a muscle until all danger was past. So they would run and hide whenever the black shadow of hawk or crow appeared, for into their tiny brains, too, is born the desire to live.

For sheer amusement we found a family of moorhen chicks hard to beat, for if you have never seen these bundles of sooty down, with grotesquely large feet and thin legs, and sporting a coral-red beak, then you have missed a sight worth watching and waiting for!

But let us return to the " sea-crow ", as the black-headed gull is often called—partly due to the noise it makes and partly on account of the way it mingles with the rooks in the autumn and winter fields, following the ploughs in huge flocks. Many people do not recognize the black-headed gull in winter, for then it is minus its chocolate-brown head, which it only acquires during the breeding season. It is certainly one of the most useful birds that the farmer has as a visitor to his fields, for it devours an enormous number of pests, such as leather-jackets and wire-worms. It is also a useful scavenger, and although it eats a little grain I think it can be forgiven for this.

YOUNG GULL

It is a queer thing, but have you noticed on our travels that the gull we have seen most as we came along the coast-roads was not the black-headed but a rather larger grey-backed gull? This is the herring gull, and it is found scattered all along our coasts. A group of these birds have the habit of sitting on an old fishing boat and " screaming their heads off " at one another, and a fine noise they can make, too! It is not until the birds are in their fourth or fifth year that they obtain their full grey and white plumage, with yellow beak and pink legs. Before that time their coats are mottled with brown.

TERNS

Above the screaming mass of gulls we have aroused, fly a group of birds which resemble nothing so much as huge white swallows, with long taper-ing wings and forked tails. These are common terns, which come to the marsh every spring from Africa. They are members of a large family, and are delicate, beautiful birds; they are known as sea swallows. After a short search we find several nests among the sea-pinks : just a few pieces of reed scraped together to form a saucer-like nest. In these are the very attractive, sharp-pointed eggs, greenish in colour and heavily mottled with black. It is amazing how well both nests and eggs blend into their surroundings and become almost invisible. It is not long before we manage to find one or two youngsters, attractive bundles of yellow fluff with big paddle feet and a feeble chirp. We place one or two on a piece of sandy rocky ground, and it is amazing how the mottled colouring of the chick blends into the natural colourings of its surroundings.

Altogether there are five species of terns which visit our coasts for a brief stay each summer, but the ones we find are the most common, having a grey back and wings, a black cap, white tail, and whitish underparts, with a coral-red beak with a black tip. It is very difficult to distinguish from the Arctic tern, but the sandwich tern, another and more common variety, can be spotted because of its greater size and shorter tail. It is altogether a heavier bird and fairly widely distributed. I always think that it is a " red-letter day " when I manage to spot a roseate tern, a lovely bird, distinguished by its pale, delicate-pink under-parts, black bill, shorter wings, and lovely long forked tail.

On the edge of the marshland runs a stretch of sandy shingle, covered with hundreds of pieces of flotsam and jetsam flung up and left by the spring flood-tides. Here, too, we find more nests of the tern, being merely hollows scooped in the sand, although some of the parents have shown an urge to decorate their nests with rings of broken sea-shells round the edge. We are away from the gulls by this time, and their deafening clamour is dying down as one after another settle once more on the eggs. We are not left in peace, however, for the new tern colony now takes up the fight, and it is remarkable the way these lovely sea swallows attack us, yelling their high-pitched cries as they swoop.

Both the gulls and terns have many enemies, chief of which is probably he huge, sombre, lesser black-backed gull, which is a real bully, and vicious, and makes short work of any eggs which are left unattended for any length of time. The very large greater black-backed gull is the real murderer of the tribe, however, and often eats birds and gull youngsters. Woe betide the wounded duck that is limping away from a charge from a wild-fowler if it is spotted by one of these birds, for it will be swooped upon and eaten in a short time. This gull nests away from all others, as you can well imagine!

We sit on a large piece of cast-up timber whilst we eat our tea, and as we sit quiet, the noise and bustle that we have known all afternoon fades; it is possible once more to pick out the calls of the red-shank, curlew and snipe. High above our heads, and flying in ever widening circles, " drum " a pair of snipe, small brown birds, with sharply angled wings, a very long straight beak, and long legs. The " drumming " which is such a characteristic feature of this marsh-bird has caused many a heated argument among bird-watchers as to its cause. However, it has been established now that the sound is made by the two extended outer tail feathers, which vibrate very rapidly when the bird is in flight, and cause this very peculiar bleating sound.

The warm May sun beats down upon us, making the whole marsh shimmer with heat haze. It is a good thing that I know the one safe route, much travelled over the years by sheep, that leads back across the marsh to the mainland, for the boat by this time is high and dry on the mud. It is amazing how quickly the tide, once it starts to ebb, will turn a well-filled channel into a deep bed of black mud into which it would be quite possible to disappear. It is a bad thing to be caught out on the

SNIPE

marsh at night, because then the " marsh-gas " rises from the wet soil, and there is danger in every step unless you are absolutely certain of your way.

Danger seems very far away, however, as we revel in the warm afternoon sun and lazily watch a red-shank that alights on the edge of the mud flat near us without becoming aware of our presence. I have always had a " soft spot " for the red-shank, with its very long spindly red legs, nobbly knee-joints, and long red beak, with which it is forever probing in the mud and water for marine insects. In common with the curlew, it, too, has a very lonely, wild call which seems exactly to match its surroundings, and, like the snipe, it certainly knows how to hide its eggs in a loosely made nest of grass carefully hidden in a thick grass clump. It takes a great deal of patience, coupled with a little luck, to locate one of these nests, but the sight of the eggs is worth the trouble, for they are very similar to those of the lapwing, *very* pointed, and beautifully blotched and marked with dark brown or black on a greenish or olive background.

Many is the time I have found, after a very long search, the four lovely eggs of the lapwing, open to the sky and merely laid, points inward, on two or three pieces of grass in the impression left by a horse's hoof in a low-lying, swampy field. Yet, so amazingly well did the eggs blend with their surroundings, that I have walked within a foot of them and yet passed by! So it is with all these marsh-dwellers ; both their eggs and youngsters are planned by protecting Nature to blend wonderfully into the ground on which they are laid.

You know, there is scarcely any spot, from the tallest cliff or tree down to a hole in a river-bank, that is not selected by some bird or other as a suitable site for bringing up a family, and many is the time when I have found normally shy birds select the most fantastic places to build their nests, places that were within a few feet of busy traffic or where people were continually passing. Some birds simply cannot have too open a position for nesting, such as the lapwing, while others like to get as far away from sight and sound of the outside world as they can. The kingfisher and sandmartin are good examples of this, for both these birds perform really wonderful feats of engineering by digging themselves deep tunnels in a river or sandbank for their nesting sites. The eggs are then laid at the end of these tunnels, which are about three feet in length, and the sitting bird hides herself away in this dark hole until the eggs are hatched.

LONG TAILED TIT

The feats of architecture that are performed by some of our small birds are certainly amazing in the extreme, and I am sure neither you nor I would want to attempt the terrific job of collecting the materials that go to form the wonderful nest of the long-tailed tit. A pair of these lovely, delicately pink-coated little birds, with their very long dark tails, have taken a fancy to a sheltered corner at the bottom of the field in which the caravan is now resting. We will rig up a hide, which is something you must do if you really want to get to know your birds at close quarters, and spend several hours watching this hard-working pair of tiny birds bringing masses of feathers, hairs, moss, lichen, and grass to weave cunningly around and between three forking twigs in a hawthorn bush. With wonderful skill and patience they will weave and mould their material, using only their small beaks as tools, until gradually it grows into a round ball, about the size of a cricket ball, with a small hole near the top. Within this beautifully soft nest the hen bird will lay about twelve very tiny white eggs, with shells so thin that the contents make them pink-tinted.

There are quite a number of birds, however, that do not build nests at all, or, at any rate, not what I should call much of a nest if I were a young bird just popping out of the egg! That pair of brown owls, John, that float around the caravan in the dusk like huge brown moths, make a pretty poor show of their homework, for they merely lay their white eggs on a few cast-up pellets of undigested fur and bones in some hollow tree.

Thrushes and blackbirds build a fairly solid, substantial nest of woven grasses, but the thrush makes a really solid job of it by lining the inside with a coating of mud, which the hen bird carries to the nest by the beakful, and then when she has given the whole a rough coating she makes the wall quite smooth by turning round and round, using her breast feathers like a trowel.

But enough of this for the moment. Let us away back to the caravan for a very early supper, after which we will try our hand at building a hide to watch a pair of little owls, which I know will provide us with some good night sport.

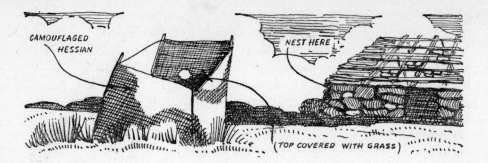

CAMOUFLAGED HESSIAN

NEST HERE

(TOP COVERED WITH GRASS)

CHAPTER VII

A Night Bird-Watching

BUILDING A "HIDE"—THE HOME OF THE RINGED PLOVER—BRAVE BIRD-PARENTS—
BIRDS CAN'T COUNT—WE SPY BY NIGHT

You know, John, this business of building a hide can be very tricky, but also very interesting, as it gives you the chance to prove how good you are at woodcraft. I think we have both learned how valuable it is to be able to keep absolutely still when watching a bird or animal, but although that is all right when we are just watching from afar it simply is no use whatever just sitting down in front of a nest or badger's hole and expecting the owner to go calmly about his business as though we were miles away!

No, John, if we are going to study that pair of little owls the job has to be done properly, and we shall need quite a deal of patience, as you cannot make a wild bird or animal do what *you* want!

Right! The first thing to do is to show you the nest, which I was fortunate enough to find the other afternoon when you were down by the river. I was walking across the large field near the caravan when I noticed a little owl fly out silently from a thick bush near a low stone hut. He was in too much of a hurry to worry about me, however, as a mob of yelling small birds were on his tail. It always amuses me the way these small birds get their own back whenever they find an owl asleep in a bush or tree in the daytime.

I went over to the bush, found several cast-up pellets on the ground, and after searching round for a while eventually found the nest under a loose slate in the gap between two moss-covered stones. From the semi-darkness of the hole two huge, angry round eyes glared at me, and I knew that the hen bird must be sitting tight on her eggs. Carefully noting the spot, I came away as quietly as possible.

Now I think, John, that it is about time we tried our hand at making a hide as near the nest as possible so that we can learn of the habits of a bird that since it was introduced into England from abroad in the latter part of the last century has multiplied and spread to a terrific extent, and has made many enemies. It is little larger than a thrush, really, being about nine inches in length, and is dark greyish-brown in colour, flecked with white. It is certainly no favourite among my gamekeeper and poultry-farmer friends, who readily accuse it of many attacks on their chicks. However, as in so many other cases, it is a case of " give a dog a bad name ", and difficult afterwards to turn it into a good one!

I have had the chance on several occasions to watch little owls when they had young to feed, and I have found that small mice, beetles, earthworms, moths, earwigs, and daddylonglegs form the main diet of this bird. I really don't think that any farmer has much to grumble at in that list, as none of them are friends of his!

Anyway, John, I hope we shall be able to see something of its meals for ourselves as soon as we have turned ourselves into two " invisible men ".

The evening is warm and quiet, one of those lovely evenings that make being in the country such a pleasure, when we reach the nesting site. Around the old stone hut are several low bramble-bushes, and it is by one of these that I decide we should have the hide. Sticking four bamboo posts, about four feet long, about a foot into the ground and forming a square large enough to allow us both to crouch within, I drape round a strip of green hessian, around and over which we soon arrange brambles and grasses until the whole thing looks quite natural. But now this is where the patience part comes in, for we shall have to leave our hide until at least tomorrow evening, by which time the birds will have become used to the sudden appearance of an extra bush!

The moon is large, white and almost blinding, as we eventually reach tne caravan, and I am glad to see that the fire is not completely out. A few moments' brisk blowing, and we have a cheerful little blaze, over which the billycan is soon hung for our supper cocoa. The air has turned very cold, as it always does in the countryside after a warm day, and we are glad to fold blankets round us as we huddle round the fire. The noises of the night reach us, and as we are near the marshlands it is from there that the cries, lonely and weird in the darkness, sound most clearly.

Above us, far away in the deep velvety blackness of the night sky, the stars of the Great Bear and Orion glitter clear and bright. A faint trace of the smell of seaweed comes from the marshes and mingles with the wood-smoke. It is the time to enjoy most of all in the world of the outdoors, and as we sip our steaming cups of cocoa we do not talk much but rather listen to those hosts of queer noises that the darkness always seems to magnify.

It seems that we have been sleeping but a few moments when a finger of pale pinkish light shines through the window of the caravan and tells us that it is again dawn. The air is raw and cold in the dawn light, and the grass underfoot is heavy with a million tiny rainbows of glistening dew. But it is the glory of the dawn sun over the marshland that holds us spellbound. Streaks of purple, red and then gold light up the east sky, and from a thousand throats the dwellers of the marsh call their greeting to another day. The rays of the early sun reach the caravan as we prepare our breakfast fire, and the warmth is very welcome.

There is no breeze, and the channels across the marsh glisten like ribbons of silver. Along the edges of the mud-flats hundreds of waders search for their breakfasts, and we can now just see our small boat floating quietly at the end of its mooring rope. The morning has all the promise of a fine day to be, and it is to the haunt of the charming little ring plover, handsome in a coat of black and white with a large black bib, that I want us to go.

Jutting out like an arm into the sea is a sandy spit of land, and it is here that the plovers nest. There is the same commotion from thousands of angry gulls as we near the boat, but we are not interested in them today, and very soon we have left them behind as we sail over the dead

calm water to the haunt of the ringed plover. To see these plump little birds as they run about the beach one would think they are clumsy, but to see their courting dance is to witness a very dainty exhibition. Both the male and female take part in this dance, for when the female accepts her mate they both celebrate by standing on tip-toe with upraised wings, while they seem to sail along the sand with a movement that is full of grace. All the while they utter a delightful yodelling song as they dance together. The cock bird, too, has a habit of turning round and round making depressions in the sand, after which the hen bird makes a tour of inspection and eventually selects one for her use. This the birds usually line with pieces of broken shell.

A crow sails over our heads as we approach the spit of land, and dives down towards where we imagine the nests to be. Immediately dozens of plovers rise with an agitated rush of wings, and the crow, with a loud " krak " of disgust, makes off.

The sand on the spit feels warm underfoot, and it is not long before we find our first nests. We have to look pretty hard, though, for the eggs closely resemble the pebbles that are lying all around.

You know, John, the plover, like the lapwing, makes a very good parent, and when there are young about the old birds will sham all sorts of injuries in order to keep an enemy away from the youngsters. They will limp along the ground dragging a wing that appears to be broken, yet somehow just managing to keep one jump ahead of their pursuer. The youngsters themselves are almost the colour of the sand, and they disappear at an amazing rate when they hear the alarm call of their parents.

Waders have the habit of sleeping standing on one leg, yet if you watch a flock of plovers asleep you will notice that every now and then

LAPWINGS

they all move forward as if under orders. Perhaps it is just a single hop, or they may take a step forward with both feet. Yes, they are certainly most amusing and entertaining little birds to watch, and the sun is swinging towards the west before we eventually leave the marshland once more and return to the caravan, with a hearty appetite for tea.

I had arranged with Moley Joe, one of the local characters, and whose knowledge of the ways of the birds and beasts of his neighbourhood is profound, to come with us this evening. It is a peculiar thing, and a fact which shows how small is the average bird's ability to count, that although three people may approach a hide in front of a nest, so long as *one* walks away the parents are quite satisfied and will return to the nest as soon as the solitary intruder is safely out of the way.

I have watched little owls many times before, and have found that although they are sometimes seen about in the daylight they very seldom feed before dusk, so it is no use our cramping ourselves into the hide too early on this lovely evening.

Owls, John, as well as many hawks, begin to brood their eggs as soon as the first one is laid, so perhaps in our nest we may find an egg just laid, one just chipping, and a spitting, hungry youngster. The first chick hatches in about a month, and the others at intervals. This is just another example of the way that Nature has provided for a " staggering " of the needs of the family, for although very young owls may be satisfied with caterpillars and other similar small fry at first, very soon they begin to want voles and mice, and these take a good deal of catching, even for a silent-winged owl. As the

LITTLE OWL

parents are away for longer and longer periods as more voles are needed to quieten the youngsters already growing, the remaining eggs are kept warm by these youngsters.

SPARROWS

So you can see how well it all works out for all concerned. It stands to reason that owls cannot lay a great many eggs in each clutch, for I dread to think of the enormous amount of hunting they would have to do to feed a large family! Owls have big appetites, you know, John, as I well remember when I had Old Joey, my brown pet owl, who used to gulp down young sparrows without doing more than give a few solemn blinks.

It certainly would not do for many of the smaller birds to form a trade union, for it is certain that they would never be able to keep to the hours permitted; at any rate, not when they have young to feed! From the very first streaks of dawn until dusk has fallen—and that can be a very large slice out of the twenty-four hours—the parents are on the never-ending search for food. What a tiring sight it must be every time the parent returns to the nest, to gaze down into the ever-open yellow gaping throats of the youngsters!

Even here it is a case of the survival of the fittest, for a weakling that fails to raise his head to the same level as the others is soon doomed to starvation. If a nestling falls from the nest it, too, is doomed. Although

OWL'S EGGS IN BARN

it may lie wriggling on the ground below the nest, neither parent will pay it the least attention.

The sun sinks lower in the west, and along the now dusty lane we see a lone figure approaching. It is Moley Joe, and very soon the three of us are heading for the haunt of the little owls. As soon as we enter the field in which the old stone hut is situated, one of the owls begins to sound the alarm. It is a very queer call, rather like a high-pitched catcalling, " kee-ow, kee-ow ". This call grows ever more excited as we approach the hide, but as Joe's figure grows smaller as he leaves the field the owls settle down once more.

It is cramped in the hide, but we are well hidden and have two good observation holes from which we can watch the nest.   After a short

THE VIEW FROM THE HIDE

while one of the parents glides silently to the hut, perches for a moment on one of the old stones, and then drops down underneath the slate with a large cockchafer beetle in his wicked-looking hooked beak. As soon as the old bird appears at the nest, the youngsters—and we have seen that there are two of them—begin calling. They raise themselves up, and cry with a kind of snoring call rather like that made by young barn owls.

The shadows thrown by the elms grow ever longer, until finally the trees stand out starkly against the last streaks of grey light in the west sky. The owls come and go, unaware of our presence, and very soon it grows too dark for us to see the food that they bring. It is so quiet in the hide that we can hear the scratching of claws on stone as the parents alight.

All along the hedgerow rabbit families, with old bucks on guard, are feeding, and in a nearby coppice the liquid notes of the nightingale are being thrown to the skies. Feeling very cramped and stiff, and not a little chilled, for it is getting late, we eventually crawl from the hide.

There is a loud and oft repeated " churrr, churrr " from a brown nightjar—or goat sucker, as old country folk still call it—and I know that in the same coppice that the nightingale has its cosy little nest the two eggs of the nightjar will be lying in a mere scrape in the ground. This is another example of a bird that fits in beautifully with its surroundings when it is at rest on its eggs, for its mottled and barred coat harmonizes exactly with the dead twigs and grasses around. So do the eggs, for that matter, and they are extremely difficult to find. I do not think there is any bird with such a huge mouth for its size as the nightjar, for it catches its food whilst on the wing, as do swallows and swifts. For this reason it has a mass of long hairs, all facing inwards, in its throat, and these form a trap for every insect caught, from which it is impossible to escape.

Imagine, John, that we have placed one of the owl's eggs, which are pure white, alongside one of the nightjar's. It stands out so clearly that it is impossible to miss, and you will find this business of eggs that are hidden from sight being white in colour repeated over and over again. You see, there is no need for any protective markings and ground colour when the eggs are laid in a hole in a tree or bank, yet every bird that lays its eggs where they could be easily seen by a host of enemies has provided them with a coloured shell that admirably suits their neighbourhood. Oh, yes, I know there are exceptions. The woodpigeon and turtle-dove lay pure-white eggs in nests that are merely a shaky collection of twigs thrown together in the fork of a tree. But there are exceptions to almost every rule in this world, and I do not think that many of the eggs of the yellowhammer—or scribble-lark, as it is often called—would escape detection if it were not for the mass of scribbly dark markings which cover the eggs and blend them in so well with the grasses of the hedgerow banks in which this bird nests.

But come, John; this is a subject we could discuss for many, many hours. I think it is much better to leave it for tonight, for the hour is late and we have a long day ahead of us tomorrow. Good night!

CHAPTER VIII

Gipsies and their Trade Tricks

COMPANIONING WITH THE GIPSIES—SECRETS OF THEIR CRAFTS—TRAPPING THE VELVET
MOLE—RAT-CATCHING WITH TOM—MICE AND MEN

Perhaps it is because we look like gipsies—we are both brown
enough, and the caravan does not look as fresh as it did at first—
that we are hailed in a deep, foreign-sounding voice as we draw
level with a group of caravans scattered about a grassy field in the lovely
Kentish countryside, through which we have been jingling now for the
past week.

"Ahoy there!" I reply, and with a "whoa, Robby" the caravan
halts and we jump down.

The man who had hailed us stops at his job for a moment and grins
a welcome, which is more than his snarling mongrel dog does, but we
prevent a contest between him and Toby, and accept with many thanks
a mug of tea from a steaming pot. Tea is always welcome to us on these
hot, dusty afternoons.

All around the gipsy's feet lay hundreds of white shavings from the
twigs he is shaping into clothes-pegs, one of the most profitable of his
many activities. After roughly whittling the peg with a bone-handled
knife, he cut out a tongue-shaped piece and slit the peg about half-way
up its length. When he had made a good pile of these, he nailed round
each peg a little tin ring to prevent the peg's splitting right through, and
the job was done.

But pegs are not the only objects the other members of the camp band
are making, mostly at no cost to themselves. Some are busy making
flower-stands out of old baskets, putting the baskets into little holders

of greenwood twigs, bound together in the form of a tripod. Some of them have ferns they have dug up from the nearby wood, and these they are fixing in the baskets, among some moss and ivy.

Others, mostly the younger members, who seem to find their play in some useful work, are making twig-shaving flower-heads, carefully splitting up a twig into a large number of shavings, which curl round, and when painted look exactly like a large flower-head.

"You're a busy crowd," I observe to the gipsy, "and I see your materials don't cost you very much!"

The gipsy chuckles. "Lor' bless you, it 'ud be a hard life if we had to pay for everything, mister. As it is, you might like to cross my José's hand with silver just for luck."

I resign myself to what I knew would happen in a few minutes after our resting here, and after producing a sixpence and presenting it to the eager José, I receive a "Good luck to you, mister!" in exchange. We can see this isn't the first time she has struck this bargain, by a long way!

The gipsy, whom a mahogany-faced woman we take to be his wife calls Tom, thaws out still further after I have treated Dana and Sue, who turn up from apparently nowhere, in the same way as José, and begins to tell us some of the camp's activities, in response to our questioning.

"Well now, come hoppin' time most of us 'll be busy workin' all the hours of daylight there are, and the little 'uns do their bit too. Rare handy they come at strippin' the stalks. We're just a coupla families in this camp, and during the year we'll cover many a mile. Come harvest there's many a man that's mighty glad of our help, and down country we usually have a go at the strawberry crop. Hoppin' is the time when we meet up with some of the other families, though, and we make quite a party of it at night."

He goes on to tell us, with a twinkle in his eye, that they have to find their food "where it grows", mostly, and game birds' eggs, rabbits, hares, and even the carefully preserved pheasants and partridges themselves, fall victims to their cunning fingers. I think of our friend, Fred Stokes, as Tom tells us a few poaching adventures of which he is particularly proud, and how he would be fuming if he could hear those stories.

The women of the family, in multicoloured shawls, ear-rings, and cheap jewellery, with bright scarves over their black hair, go round the villages from door to door with odd assortments of saleable goods, pegs, flowers, cheap tin kettles, crockery, dish mops, and other things, and it is rarely that they do not have by far the better of the exchange with the housewife. Their glib tongue is only equalled by their amazing invention when their palm has been crossed with silver in exchange for a "fortune telling", which the housewife usually believes, as gipsies, with their sharp eyes and knowing looks, are regarded with no little awe in the country.

Gipsy-made bee-skeps are one of the things they make—in a style all their own, too. As we are both anxious to see one of these made, Tom obliges. He takes some wheat-straw—we do not ask him how he came by it—combs it out straight, twists it with a long rope, which he binds round and round with bands of brambles. We watch with great attention whilst he cuts a long trail of bramble, removes all the thorny parts and cleverly slits it all down its length. Then he scrapes away all the soft pithy part inside until he is left with the tough bark part. The straw, after he has bound it with this tough binding, he works into the shape of a skep basket.

Another useful article which is appreciated by the country housewife, and which costs Tom nothing to make, is the besom broom; and these brooms, made of long, springy birch-twigs, make a really " clean sweep " when it comes to turning out the shed or getting the autumn leaves into a tidy heap.

We sit chatting longer, and eventually I say I think we will put up here for the night. Why go farther? We have found some interesting companions, and we are ever ready to learn more country secrets. I think, too, that Tom, who tells us he is going mole-catching, will take us with him after I have again " crossed his palm ".

MOLE - SHOWING HUGE FORE PAW

We get out our goods and pans and make ourselves at home, and we are soon accepted as one of the camp. We cook our meal over the blazing open fire while you bombard Tom with questions about the mole.

" Ah! That little velvet 'un—mouldwarp, us'un call it—can get out of sight quicker'n you can say knife," Tom says. " He's got all his strength and weight in his front paws, and he don't put much faith in his back feet. His two front feet are like spades, and the claws be as sharp as chisels. He can shovel the earth behind him at a rare rate, but he never gets dirt in his eyes because they are sunk right into his head, and he is almost blind. He cer-tainly can't be called deaf, though, and he seems to hear with his whole body. You know his velvety coat? Well, the short hair grows up-right, and lies as smooth one way as another if you stroke it, which is very useful when he wants to go backwards, 'cause he fits like a glove into the tunnel he digs. He uses that long pointed nose of his for boring and hunting for worms, 'cause he lives mostly on worms and slugs, beetles and a lot of other insects. You want to watch him when he grabs a fat worm; he'll nose around it, shake it like a cat with a mouse, bite and trample on it and then cram it into his mouth. Why d'you reckon he does all that, young 'un?"

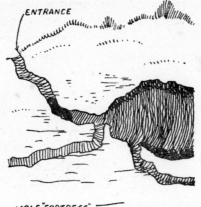

MOLE "FORTRESS"

You have been gazing intently at Tom all the time he has been telling you this, but at this question you shake your head, and Tom continues: "Well, a worm lives on earth, y'know, and all those little piles of fine soil you see about the fields are what have passed through the worm's body. 'Course, now, the mole doesn't want to eat all the earth and the worm, so he rips a bit off the worm's tail, and squeezes out the earth as he eats his meal. Sometimes, y'know, moles tunnel right under a partridge's nest and then he will make short work of the eggs."

"Where does the mole have his family?" you ask, with great interest.

"Usually at the end of April there is a litter of four little 'uns, and in the autumn mouldwarp makes himself a sort of fortress. He hollows out a kind of cave just under the ground and makes corkscrewy tunnels through which he pushes the earth. This fort is quite a size, y'know, young 'un, about a foot high and three feet across. Down he takes grass and leaves and makes a cosy nest, for he believes in comfort; but he's a wary little beggar, too, 'cos he keeps a run ready for escape if necessary. They have more to put up with than my traps, y'know, 'cos owls will pick one up quick as light, and the ol' fox will sometimes dig 'em out. Cats, dogs and weasels keep 'em on the watch, too."

Tom dries up for a bit then, for he is collecting his traps, and is eager to collect the money he will get for the dead bodies and for the plush-looking skins.

He does not set his traps in the new surface runs we see, but in some of the main highways, which may be used for years. He just makes an opening large enough for the trap to work, and carefully covers it to keep out all light. Tom uses some of the old country traps, which are fitted with string nooses and are sprung by a trigger, which releases a three-

NETTING

GIN TRAP
USUALLY COVERED
WITH GRASS

BOX TRAP FOR LIVE CATCHING

foot stick of springy ash, one end of which is in the ground and the other fast in the noose. This " bender " pulls the noose tight round the mole's neck, and " he's a gonner ", as Tom says.

" I've caught thousands of they like this," Tom says, " but I reckon more get killed by flood water than by my traps."

He put up his traps with all the cunning of an old hand. Very soon he has finished, and we return to the camp, with you eager to see how we have fared in the morning.

Darkness, with the cheerful open fire, deepens very quickly, and it seems such a short time before a thump at the caravan door tells us that Tom is up and ready to visit his traps.

The morning is quiet and full of the promise of a lovely day ahead.

We make short work of our dressing, and set off with Tom to where the host of molehills cover the field in which he has set his traps.

He has had luck, and, chuckling to himself, he collects the little plump moles.

Back at the camp, he expertly rolls off the skins, and goes off to collect his " wages " from the farmer whose land he is trying to rid of moles.

We walk with him, for you are eager to learn much more from this country expert. Tom seems quite proud of the way you are drinking in all the knowledge he pours out unceasingly, and of things which you are scribbling into your book.

Toby and the mongrel dog have chummed up, and suddenly there is a terrific yelp from both dogs as they tear off after a brown, scampering form they have flushed from a cornstack.

" There goes one of the worst enemies old Farmer Smithers has on this 'ere land," says Tom, " and I reckon as 'ow I'll be a-dealin' with a few of them."

It was a brown rat, and was giving the dogs a good chase before Toby finally seized it by the back of the neck and shook it furiously until it hung limp and lifeless.

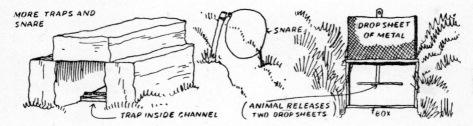

MORE TRAPS AND SNARE — SNARE — DROP SHEET OF METAL — TRAP INSIDE CHANNEL — (ANIMAL RELEASES TWO DROP SHEETS) — BOX

" Rats and mice cost the country millions of pounds every year," I say, " and, you know, some people who hate the very sight of them are the first to encourage them. Poultry-farmers are perhaps as bad as anyone when they overfeed the fowls at night. When the weather is very bad, too, rats will attack and kill the roosting chickens, suck the eggs, and cause a lot of damage unless they are promptly dealt with. You can always tell a rat's killing by the way it gnaws at its victim's crop."

" A rare good trap for they varmint is to set up three bricks like a tunnel, put a dead fowl in t'middle, and set a trap as light as you can at each end," says Tom. " If it's in a good spot you can catch dozens like this, but if one gets away with the loss of a foot, mebbe, the little beggar isn't likely to be caught again—no, sir! "

" A case of once bitten twice shy," you say, with a grin.

" A rare scandal the way people hoard up rats," Tom continues. " Jest you look around here now; all those stacks, old barns, and hedge-banks get choked with 'em, unless a real good clean sweep is made. It ain't no good a-messin' about catchin' one here and one there. You know, young 'un, they breed at such a rate that if you leave jest one pair they'll soon make up for all you've caught. The great thing is to know where exactly to put the traps, and jest how to deal with them, for if you make a mistake then you're in for a rare old time, for the rat is a cunnin' critter to deal with. Now rats 'll either bore out a tunnel for themselves, a little larger than a half-crown in size, or use an old rabbit's hole. You can always tell if rats are using a rabbit's warren, if you see connecting runs going from one hole to another, for rabbits come out for a good nibble, not just to pop into the next hole. There's a tidy difference between the runs made by rats and rabbits, too, young 'un. If you see a sort of shallow rut, it's been made by rats passing backwards and forwards pressing the grass down with their bodies; but jest you look at all the rabbit runs you find and you'll see they are flat and level, 'cos a rabbit runs with his body high from the ground."

Tom pauses for a moment, then carries on: " Another little tip is that rabbits don't stop up any of their holes, but rats will, and if the rats have left that bit of ground you'll see that where they have run about at the entrance of the holes a green fungus soon appears—just what you'd expect a rat to leave behind! "

We wait for a while for Tom whilst he negotiates with the farmer, and when he comes from the farmhouse he tells us he has the job of clearing the rats from the farm.

" Quite a sizeable little ol' job, too," he says.

We go on.

" Best time for getting the rats is at threshing," Tom explains. " Jest afore stack is to be threshed I allus go around smoking 'em out of their holes and drivin' 'em to the stack. Then on threshing day a piece of half-inch wire netting is set up all round the stack, with the top bent over to stop the varmints jumpin' over. Then, be golly, there's some fun when the threshin' starts and the dogs are turned loose on 'em."

He looks at his mongrel as he says this, and the dog seems to understand just what he means, for it seems fairly to dribble with the thought of rat feasts it has had in the past.

" For huntin' in the hedge-banks, me little ol' Judy 'ere takes some beatin'," continues Tom, " but I also use ferrets, a good spade, a small axe and an iron bar. Yer need a real good trained dog that'll wait quietly until the rats are right away from their holes before they run. Not like your dog, mister, 'cos altho' he's a rare good runner he makes enough row to scare all the rats for miles."

We all laugh at this, for it is certainly true that Toby is *not* quite the ideal quiet hunter, although the way he grubs things out of the undergrowth is amazing.

" Well, yer puts the ferrets in the holes, see? " says Tom, who seems determined to teach us thoroughly, and is not to be stopped. " Then, like as not, yer can start a whole lot movin' by probin' about with the iron bar down a burrow, for rats hate this. Then it's the turn of the dogs when the rats are in the open, and I've caught thousands this way."

" That's not much good for burrows that are simply honeycombed with holes, or for holes among large rocks or roots, is it? " I ask at this stage.

Tom shakes his head.

" No, mister, but if you plug up all the holes except one and then squirt in some of that there stuff they call sulphur somethin'—dioxide I think it is, altho' I can't never recollect these fancy names—then you'll kill every one. Tar and paraffin, too, are good for rootin' them out."

We go on to talk about rats and mice and how they came to be such a nuisance here. About the seventeenth century the black rat was the great pest in England and the dreaded carrier of the Black Death, as the plague was called. In 1728 the brown rat made its appearance here, and being a very tough little beggar it had become a real menace within fifty years. Rats begin to breed at about four months, and at all seasons of the year, so if nothing was done to keep them down the country would soon be overrun with them.

The house-mouse is very like a miniature rat. It has followed man all over the world, and, like the rat, it multiplies at a terrific rate. In the fields and gardens the destructive but pretty little long-tailed fieldmouse is the chief rodent. It has a light-brown coat, with white underparts and feet and very large eyes. If the garden-peas are disappearing at a fast rate, you can be fairly sure that the thief is the long-tailed mouse! In autumn it gathers a good store of nuts, haws and seeds into a warm corner and settles down for the winter. Sometimes a good number of mice pool their stores, and share the eatables in a pretty fair way. Often in spring the man who has stored potatoes in sacks will find that these have been nibbled through and a great many of the potatoes are nothing but skin. Look out for old birds' nests in winter, for these are often used by mice for their feeding places, and occasionally a nest is roofed over with moss to form a permanent home. The youngsters, however, are born in an underground nest of dry grass, and there are several litters a year.

RAT

Chiefly in the south of the country is the gay harvest mouse, with one exception the smallest of our mammals. It is golden-brown and white underneath, and the nest is a beautifully built ball of grass woven between corn stalks. The mouse is so light that it climbs a wheat stem without bending it, and, like the fieldmouse, it stores up seeds for winter use.

The sleepy little dormouse, which is getting rather scarce now, is a lover of thick hedgerows and copses where hazels are plentiful, for it is a heavy eater of the nuts. It spends the daytime in deep sleep and makes a cosy nest almost three inches across of moss and dry grass. This is often placed high in a bush, and when the dormouse is at home he closes the little entrance hole. The nursery home is sometimes built underground. For six months of the year the dormouse goes into a deep sleep, and the little creature feels practically dead. Getting ready for this, the dormouse eats a great deal and puts on a lot of fat. It also lays in a good stock of nuts and wakes up on a warm winter evening and has a good feed. It also eats insects, fruit and seeds as well as nuts.

Then, too, there are the voles, who differ from the mice by having blunt muzzles, small ears hidden in their fur, and shorter tails.

The one that causes most damage to crops is the field-vole, which is very different from a fieldmouse in looks, although country folk often call it the short-tailed fieldmouse. It has a more stumpy, rounder body, no ears that can be seen, and a very short one-inch tail. The natural enemies of the voles and all mice are owls, stoats, weasels and hawks, and if these are killed off too much by keepers then the voles multiply into a plague that will clear whole crops before they can be checked.

The bank-vole, which is found in woods and hedge-banks, is smaller than the field-vole, and is bright chestnut above and white below.

There is just one other, the large water-vole, often called a water-rat. Its food consists of the juicy stems of water-reeds or plants, and if one can be approached very quietly you can hear his sharp teeth ripping at the hard outer skin. It drops with a " plop " when disturbed and swims silently under the water until it pokes up its nose a safe distance away. I always think they are like little beavers to watch, and they use their hand-like paws very cleverly.

If you really set out to watch some of these interesting little creatures you will find that they have a great deal of intelligence packed away, and you will need to be very sharp, too, for their eyes do not miss very much that goes on around them. With a kestrel hanging over them by day, watching the grass for every movement, and the owls by night, they cannot afford to be half asleep when they go far afield.

CHAPTER IX

Under the Greenwood Tree

ON THE ROAD AGAIN—TREES AND HOW THEY WORK—HOW TO TELL TREES—TREE-DWELLERS AND TREE-THIEVES—TURNING TREES INTO SHIPS AND FURNITURE—HOW TO MEASURE A TREE'S HEIGHT

The heavy dew of a fine day to come was just drying from the rich summer grass when we said goodbye to Tom and the rest of the gipsy families, and it seems so quiet to be on the road again without all their chatter around us.

We have passed through some delightful country since we started, and some of our most peaceful moments have been spent in the shadow of some huge tree growing by the hedgeside. It is in such a position that we stop when the sun is very high in the sky and give Robby a rest from his steady plodding.

As we sit and dream quietly in the shade, you suddenly say, " I'd really like to know a bit more than I do about all these trees we see, Woodman. Do they serve very many useful purposes? "

" Well, John, I am glad you brought that up, for if there were no trees we should soon have the whole country like a desert. That may surprise you, but it is true, and now just pick up that oak leaf lying there and you will be feeling one of the best feeders of the soil. You see, the leaves are the most active part of any plant or tree and without them it would die. Day and night the leaves work at the task of feeding and breathing. Mineral salts are taken in by the roots from the ground, but the most important plant food, carbon dioxide, is absorbed from the air around by the leaves.

" Carbon dioxide is the stuff we breath out, isn't it, Woodman? " you ask.

" Yes, and that's where plants in a room can take in a lot of the bad air that is left after we have breathed in the oxygen and breathed out the carbon dioxide. Have you noticed, too, how the individual leaves of a tree are so formed that they overshadow each other as little as possible, so that all can catch the sun? The lower branches reach out farther than those on top for this reason. It's just the same with climbing plants, too. They twist and cling to everything, like that white bryony over there, in order to keep in the sun. You know, too, John, how the brambles work upwards, hooking on to other plants by their curved prickles. So, you see, they make up for the weakness of their stems by their persistence in using other plants and trees as props. Now, animals need carbon to live, and this they obtain from eating plants. Then, as they breathe, the animals give out carbon dioxide to the air again, and so the whole process starts again."

" Nature seems to have everything worked out so wonderfully, doesn't it, Woodman? " you say.

" Yes, John, and the leaves also clean the air we breathe, by absorbing the gas which is useless and even poisonous to both animals and ourselves, and turning it into oxygen. Leaves also have another job to do, too; they make the sap rise in the spring by this pull on the water supply of the tree. I wonder if you knew that a man can live less than five weeks without food, John? It is the tree that makes possible the growth of food by improving the quality of the earth supplying cereals, sugar, honey, fruit and nuts, and making land for grazing cattle. We could live less than five minutes without clean air, and we've seen how trees give us the oxygen we need. It is quite true to say that when the forests go, so too go the waters and fish, the game and the crops; flocks and herds all go and the land dries up to a desert.

" When the Romans came to England vast forests covered the land, but today we have lost most of these, although a few large forests still remain. Now, just jot down these details in the notebook, and as we go through that large wood you can just see ahead of us, try to pick out the various trees, and we'll pick a leaf specimen from each and press them. That's the best way to make a permanent collection and learn quickly, you know."

I pause for a while to light the old pipe, and give the small fire a stir, for a good hot drink can be cooling even on a day like this.

" Each tree has its own peculiar signs, you know, John. You can pick out the oak over there by the way that old dead branch rises out of the

leafy mass of leaves below. Once you learn to pick
that out you see it again and again in oaks. You
will usually see a pair of rooks or a hawk perched
there, too, for it makes a very good lookout post.
England has been famed for its oaks for hundreds of
years, and they usually grow to a giant size on damp
clayey soils. Beeches, John, you will find on chalk
soil, and the pines grow best in dry, sandy ground.
The oak is the only tree strong enough to throw out
its huge strong branches fifty or sixty feet hori-
zontally with the ground, and even though the snow
falls heavily in winter they resist all pressure in
their strength. It's quite cheerful in an oak-wood,
too, for there grow a mass of shrubs such as hazel
and brambles, but in beechwoods it is rather sad
and lonely. Because of the dense shade and the thick
layer of slowly decaying leaves there is no undergrowth, and the fine straight, smooth, grey trunks
have only the jays, hawks and squirrels for company.

"You can pick out a chestnut-tree by the
beautiful curves of its branches, which, like the
leaves, grow in pairs on opposite sides of the stems.
First they rise, then fall in a long curve, and finally
curve up again at the tips. The long leaves form a
thick, deep-green covering, and the mass of white
candle-like flowers that stand out all over the tree in
spring is one of the most easily seen features of the
hedgerow. The nuts in autumn are one feature you
will know, I'm sure, John, and I can well remember
when I was at school what a good trade the hot-
chestnut man did on a cold November evening when
we were waiting for the train home.

BLACK BRYONY

" There are just a few more facts I would like you to jot down about the oak before we pass on, John. The bark is very rough, and the sharply bent 'elbow pieces' on the branches were used a great deal in ship-building in olden days. The pollen-bearing catkins show in May, and the acorns come from the female flowers. In winter the twigs have clusters of small brown buds, and then you can easily see the oak apples. These are hard, woody balls, and are caused by the irritation of the eggs of a small wasp laid in the buds in winter. The ' apple ' is yellowish-green and quite soft at first, but it becomes hard about July, when the fully grown wasps have emerged."

I have been speaking very quietly and we have been keeping quite still all this time. Because of this the wild life around us has become scarcely aware of our presence, and suddenly up the rough bark of the oak a short distance away from us darts a slim chestnut-coloured form with long, black-tipped tail. We are watching a stoat, which can climb a tree in search of wood-pigeon's and other birds' eggs almost as well as a squirrel. Weasels are also expert climbers, and even the little long-tailed fieldmouse will climb a tree for the pleasure of sucking an egg.

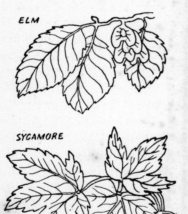

ELM

SYCAMORE

OAK

ASH

Suddenly there is a clatter and the clap of hitting wings as a woodpigeon flies from her eggs at the approach of the chestnut thief. With white wing-bars showing plainly on grey-blue wings, she is off. We keep quite still, for pigeons are some of the farmer's worst enemies, and the stoat acts as natural " keeper " by keeping them in check, although he in his turn is hunted by every gamekeeper in the land.

The stoat bolts down any hole like lightning when he is disturbed, and the weasel will even use a mouse hole, so slim is *his* body. They are very curious by nature, and no sooner do they run into a hole for safety than out pop their beady-eyed little heads. But if danger is still near they disappear again in a flash. Another little point is that although a stoat will take to a tree when chased by a dog he will never do so when surprised by man.

" Well now, John, to get back to these trees of ours. What do you think is the most common tree we have seen on our trip so far? "

You think for a moment and then say, " Well, Woodman, I think it is the elm. That's an elm over there, isn't it? "

You point to a tall, slender tree looking like a very tall umbrella in shape, and I agree with you. Wherever there are hedgerows you will find the common elm. I always think that a row of elms in winter or early spring, with their mass of thin twigs housing a host of black rooks' nests, seems to catch the very spirit of the English countryside. The trunk is tall, and the long branches usually seem to grow right upwards. They have masses of small brittle twigs at the ends, and the flowers appear in February or early March, before the small oval deep-green leaves appear. There is one thing to watch out for carefully if you pitch camp near elms: be sure that none of the branches could possibly fall on the site. Elms are notorious for the way the branches and even trunks are often completely rotten and eaten away underneath the bark, so just beware and do *not* stand under an elm even if it *is* raining hard.

The two staves, with their Y-shaped tops, which have served us so well since we started, come from the ash, which you can pick out in winter by the very " ropey " effect of the branches. They look just like old sea-soaked ropes, and have blunt ends, quite the opposite of the elms. The bark of the tall trunk is smooth and greyish in colour, and the branches are heavy and strong. At the first sign of an autumn nip in the air the leaves, which grow in pairs on each side of the long stems, fall to the ground. The black leaf buds, clustered in thick bunches near the ends of the twigs, still show dark in spring long after most other trees have opened their leaves.

Beech-leaves are shiny and bright-green when mature, and in the fall they become a rich golden-brown. The " mast " or bristly fruits, each containing three smooth, brown nuts, come from the female flowers. You can tell a hornbeam from a beech by three signs when you are at a short distance. The bark of the hornbeam, although fairly smooth, is cracked and more deeply grooved. The leaves, too, are much rougher,

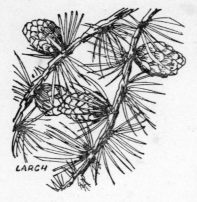

LARCH

with double "teeth", and are hairy beneath. The fruit of the hornbeam hangs in sprays from the undersides of the branches in autumn, and in winter the small branches look like a lace network against the sky.

"The trees I like best, Woodman, are those like the pines," you break in at this stage, after we have had a pause while you get some of these jottings down.

"Yes, John, and so do I, and in some of the lonely pine and larch forests in the far north where I have tramped it always thrilled me to hear the sudden deep 'swish' of the snow dropping from the heavy-laden needles. These trees belong to a class called conifers, most of which are evergreen. The leaves are only shed very slowly and not all at one time.

"The Scots pine is perhaps about the best I know for loveliness, and Norfolk is one of the best districts to study these. The turpentine and resin of the cones and twigs have a lovely healthy smell and make you want to take deep breaths when you are in a pine-wood. The trunk is tall and straight, and the rough bark is cast in large scales which leave copper or pinkish-coloured patches. The tufted, needle-like leaves grow at the ends of the radiating branches. The firs, by the way, have flat leaves growing singly on the stem. The leaves stay on the pines for about three years, and when they drop they make a very soft, springy carpet. Pine twigs and cones are excellent fire-lighters too. The cones are male and female and the latter take two years to mature. Pines grow in sandy places, and their long straight trunks are much used for scaffold and telegraph poles, masts and ladders. Pine-wood furniture and buildings have a lovely appearance—and smell, too—and from the bark and sapwood we obtain turps, tar and pitch.

"The larch, I always think, is a lovely 'fairyland' tree. Unlike the other conifers, it sheds its leaves in winter, and they lie like a fine gold soft carpet around the tree. The bark is blackish-grey and very scaly, and the feathery small needle-like leaves are a palish-green in early summer. The young cones are an attractive crimson, and the whole tree looks like a high triangle."

We have stamped out the fire, re-harnessed Robby, and are making our slow way along the country road by this time. Across our path fly three dashing black-and-white magpies, uttering their harsh chattering cries of alarm. They are young villains whose sharp eyes will be on the lookout for some of the gamekeeper's cherished possessions before long. We can just see the huge structure of black hawthorn twigs which was their home at the top of a tall tree.

A squat, red-bricked Norman church appears as we round a bend, buried deep behind a massive yew-tree. It was a favourite practice in the days when churches were used as strongholds and weapons were bows and arrows to plant yew-trees in churchyards, for it was from their springy, tough branches that the longbows were made. The branches spring from the trunk very near the ground, and the greyish, red-brown bark is scaly. The dark, glossy-green leaves are very thick, and the scarlet berries give the whole tree a somewhat sinister and unfriendly look, especially on a wet evening.

" I think the hazel is one of the most ' friendly ' kind of trees, don't you, Woodman? " you exclaim, as we near the wood and see the mass of hazel-shoots under the oaks, heavily laden with the green nuts.

" Yes, John, and one of the most useful, too. Besides providing the woodland squirrels, dormice, nuthatch and other creatures with a fine stock of winter food, the wood, being soft, very tough and not too heavy, is used for many things. Cask hoops, walking sticks, withes for tying faggots, and ' spiks ' for thatching all come from the young wood, and hurdles, cattle fences, pea sticks and bean poles also come from its shoots. Poachers sometimes set snares for rabbits by using the very springy shoots, but they are rather conspicuous. The hazel doesn't care for much heat, and grows best besides streams and on swampy ground. It grows and spreads very quickly, too, but does not live to a great age as trees go, about sixty or seventy years.

" If you watch a nuthatch, John, you will see he breaks a nut from a branch, flies to an oak, strips off the outer covering of leaves, and then very cleverly wedges the nut in a crack in the bark. Then using his bill, he bangs away at the shell until it cracks up and he is able to get at the nut. In October you can hear quite a regular tap-tap-tap, sounding like a crowd of open-air shoe-menders! "

HAZEL NUTS

As I am telling you this, I suddenly remember that we are nearing a good fishing river, and in readiness for this we set to work stripping two long pliant hazel rods, for these make excellent fishing rods.

" Those limes over there will probably be cut for building organs and making sounding-boards for pianos. Maples, because of their lovely grain, are used very largely by cabinet-makers. Planks, sweet-smelling and of a fine colour, will come from those firs and pines, and boat and waggon builders use ash, which makes the best oars and shafts. Beech, which is brittle and short-grained, is mostly used for chairs now, and carpenters' planes come from this wood, too.

" The wood from the lovely silver-birch mostly goes to the cabinet-maker, and I guess those old gateposts in that hedge came from a sweet chestnut tree, which is very tough and lasting. Railway trucks and carts are lined with willow, which will rather bend than crack under a heavy load. The best of the wood goes for cricket bats, as you probably know, John. The miners' pitprops, as well as really solid furniture, come from the oak. Perhaps you didn't know, John, that the alder, which is a real swamp-loving tree, has such sound-keeping wood under water that it is used for propping up the banks of rivers, and for making weirs and dams and piles, but if you stick a post of this wood in the ground it will rot at the level of the earth in a few months. That's a bit difficult to believe, isn't it? The elms we talked about a short time back are used a great deal in shipbuilding. It is an interesting hobby collecting small pieces of bark, wood and leaves from each tree and writing all you can find of the tree's uses by the side of the pressed leaf.

" Now for an easy way of measuring a tree. First stand with your back against it; then pace out a distance of about thirty feet from the tree. Measure your pace sometimes, so that you know roughly how much ground you cover at a time. Get into the habit of visualising what a height or length of fifty or one hundred feet looks like, so that you are able to compare other things in your mind. Anyway, John, you are a good distance from the tree. Now bend down and look through your opened legs back at the tree. Can you see the very top yet? No; then go on a few paces farther, and try again. Ah! You can just see the top twigs from between your legs. Right! Now push a twig into the ground there, and pace back to the tree. That distance will be roughly the height of the tree, John, although, of course, it will not be dead accurate."

Now, away we go once more.

CHAPTER X

Peter the Poacher Shares His Secrets

BY THE OLD MILL—PETER THE POACHER—HOW TO TICKLE TROUT—CRAYFISHING BY
MOONLIGHT—POACHING SECRETS—HANDLING WILD CREATURES

It is very quiet by the old mill. The slow-running water of the river gurgles lazily through the long overgrown waterwheel.

The air is full of those quiet droning hums that make you feel so drowsy on a warm late summer day. There is no wind, and until a flash of brilliant blue-and-red darts by very little sign of life.

" Look at *that*, Woodman! " you cry in delight at this winged gem of colour, and we keep perfectly still on the old bridge and watch.

The kingfisher, for this is what the bird is, pauses in his flight and settles on a bough overhanging the steep bank. We can just see a hole, liberally splashed on its edge with " whitewash ", and from this comes the constant chatter of youngsters waiting with ever-growing impatience to be fed the silver fish the male has gleaming in his beak.

It is getting late in the season for nesting, but the kingfisher, one of the loveliest birds we have in England, is a real hard worker, and will rear his second family in late summer. The youngsters do not start life dressed in the dull first feathers of most birds, but come out from the rather evil-smelling nesting hole in the bank of the river attired in feathers almost equal in beauty to their parents'. The female, too— unlike most hen-birds, which are very sober in their attire and leave the gay feathers to the male—is just as beautiful as her partner. But when it comes to nesting—ah, then, poor bird, she has to suffer, for whereas the hen-blackbird with her sombre brown coat, or the thrush or hedge-sparrow, can build finely constructed nests in the hedgerow, from where they can watch the outdoor world as they sit on their eggs, the kingfisher must hide her beautiful colours. So she lays her white eggs at the end of a long dark tunnel from which she can see but a tiny point of light. The youngsters—there are usually six or seven—are born on no soft bed of feathers, either, but have to get as comfortable as they can on a bed of fish-bones, which have been cast up by the parents for this purpose! It always amazes me how such gloriously coloured birds ever emerge from such a dank, evil-smelling place, but emerge they do, and no prouder parents could be found anywhere than the two old birds as they survey their blue-and-ruby family perched side by side on a bough overhanging the water.

"Do kingfishers use ready-made tunnels for their nesting holes?" you ask, as back along the stream, intent on another catch, goes the tiny fisherman.

"Well, almost always they bore their own tunnel," I tell you, "both birds helping in this work. You see, like so many other birds, each kingfisher has his own little stretch of territory, and will allow no other bird but his mate to live or fish there. Having selected a good spot, they will charge full-pelt at the bank, using their strong beak as a pick. Then, having enough earth out to allow them to grip the side with their little red feet, they turn themselves into miniature excavators, boring out the earth until they have a long tunnel. The passage they slope upwards, and it may be some three feet long. At the end they make a slight depression, and here is the nest, with no home comforts! This work takes them sometimes about three weeks, and I have often watched them hard at work from a hide close to the hole, and marvelled at their courage in tackling such a man-size job. When the hole *is* finished, however, it becomes a sort of ancestral home, and the descendants of the original owners will use it year after year, guarding it jealously from all intruders.

"During the two weeks that the hen is brooding, the mate feeds her, like a very attentive husband, but when the youngsters are a few days old both the old birds have their work cut out to keep the hungry family satisfied. The youngsters always know when Father is about, for he comes tearing downstream uttering his shrill ' peet-peet-peet ' before entering the hole. The captured fish is held lengthwise in his bill, otherwise he would never get in the tunnel at all. Then if you watch for a bit you will see him come out tail first, so tight a fit is the hole! Then one proud day out comes the boldest of the youngsters in response to the parent's repeated calls, and with his ' heart in his mouth ' he takes the greatest risk of his short life and launches himself into the air up to the branch where he can see the fish held as bait by the old bird. After that the rest follow in quick succession, and another stage in their progress has been achieved.

" The next step is teaching them to catch their own fish, and here again the parents are good teachers. Just watch that old bird now, John, and see how he goes about this fishing business. He's such a patient little fellow, you know, and his favourite dodge is to sit motionless on an old stump, or an overhanging branch, and watch with sharp eyes everything that passes beneath him. Then, down he drops with a splash, going right under the water after his prey, and comes up with a struggling minnow in his beak. Returning to his perch, he grips the fish by the tail and bangs its head soundly against the wood to ensure its quick death. Tossing it in the air, he catches it expertly and gulps it down headfirst.

" The most beautiful attitude of the 'fisher, however, John, is when he hovers like a winged jewel over the water while fishing. Then he plunges down, and rises, flinging the glittering drops of water in all directions."

I take a short breather to light up the old pipe, and after letting me have a few puffs at this you ask: " I've heard that 'fishers migrate to the sea in autumn, Woodman. Is that right? "

" Well, John, they do to a certain extent, and there is a great deal of movement around the East Coast. Something seems to tell them that they must travel to the coast in search of food, when the cold winter winds of late autumn ruffle their feathers, and the river is becoming full of dead leaves. A good many of the

—KINGFISHER AND NEST—

youngsters, especially, die in a hard winter, for they are turned out from the home waters as soon as they are able to fend for themselves. I always feel very sorry for the tiny splash of colour looking so forlorn on our lonely, wind-swept marshes in midwinter, and always feel glad when spring brings them back to the shelter of the river bank once more."

Suddenly you draw my attention to a solitary figure lying full-length

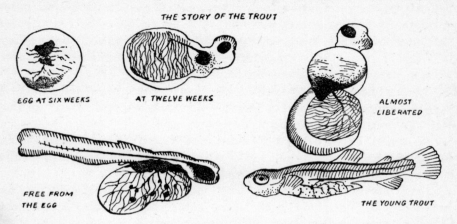

THE STORY OF THE TROUT

EGG AT SIX WEEKS   AT TWELVE WEEKS   ALMOST LIBERATED

FREE FROM THE EGG   THE YOUNG TROUT

on the river bank, with one arm deep into the placid water by an over-hanging willow.

"Ah! That will be Old Peter, I suppose, doing a bit of trout tickling!" I exclaim. "Let's go over there. He's a queer old character, and if he feels in a talkative mood he'll tell us some good stories of fishing."

With that we walk towards the still figure. At our approach he raises his head slightly, and then his wrinkled face breaks into a beaming smile as he says in a rich, deep voice, "Mornin', master, and you, too, young' un!"

"Morning, Peter!" I reply. "How do the trout like being tickled today?"

He sits up, gives a deep chuckle, and points to two good-sized trout lying by his side. "Nay so bad; 'tis rare foine weather we're havin'."

We sit by his side, and I offer him a plug of tobacco, which he accepts with gratitude.

"Do show us how you tickle trout, Peter!" you exclaim, and Peter, with a sidelong glance at me, says, "All right, young 'un, but it ain't everyone as I'll show."

With that, he bids us lie full-length on the bank, and very slowly he lowers his arm once more into the water. We keep quite quiet like this for some moments, then, right above Peter's motionless hand, glides a handsome speckled trout. Very, very slowly Peter brings up his hand and then gently tickles the trout under his belly. You can hardly believe it possible, but the trout, which will dart off like a flash at the movement of a shadow across the water, remains quite still and seems to enjoy the experience. Peter knows this, for a trout loves to rub his belly on the root of a tree or on the river bed. Very slowly the strong fingers move up the body, until with a tight hold they fasten on the gills. Then, with a sharp flick, out comes the gleaming trout to land with a thud on the grass.

" Well, I think that's amazing! " you exclaim in astonishment, and I join in congratulating Peter on his skill.

" Lookee here, marster, how'd 'ee like to come after some o' they crayfish along o' me tonight? " says Peter, now in real good humour after our praise. " Moon be just right tonight."

You are all excitement at the idea, and I agree heartily myself, for crayfish, which are like small lobsters and are found in great quantities in so many of our streams, make delicious eating.

So it is arranged, and shortly after nightfall we arrive at the bridge once more and find old Peter there complete with his dozen nets. These are home-made affairs, being constructed of circles of very stout wire, about two feet across, and covered with double strawberry netting. This sags a bit in the middle to give a shallow saucer, and in the centre of each net is tied a piece of kipper. To each ring is fastened three short lengths of string at equal distances, and these are joined to a longer piece, in the middle of which a piece of white rag is tied.

We need a dozen nets for the night's fishing, for you can never be certain in just which particular spot the crayfish will be found. In one net we may get a good haul, and a few yards farther downstream there may be none.

Without making any noise we carry the nets to the river bank, and gently lower the first net into the river. The long string is then laid straight across the grass and you can now see what the white rag is for, for it would be almost impossible to find it again in the darkness without this. At intervals of a few yards we lower our other nets until all twelve are on the river bed.

Then back we walk to where the first net was lowered, and amid rising excitement gather in the string until with a sharp flick we drop the net on to the grass. We are lucky, for holding on to the bait are some five grey-green crayfish. They do not keep still for many seconds, but begin a wild scramble back to the river. Old Peter, with long experience behind him, grasps them between finger and thumb across their backs and they are soon safe within our basket.

So we go from net to net, and by the time we reach the last we have a really heavy load.

Stacking the nets away in a hiding-place known only to himself, Peter accompanies us back along the river bank towards a tiny spot of yellow light, behind which we know that our good lady will be ready to cook our catch.

The moon has risen by this time, and we manage to lure Peter into telling us some of his poaching experiences.

" Ah, even keepers ain't what they were," says Peter. " Many's the thrill I've had outwittin' a keeper before I got home with my pockets full. Take pheasants, now. I used to attract them to the hedges by the wood over yonder with acorns and raisins. Then when they got used to goin' through safely I slung small nooses from the branches and fence wires. Then, as the pheasants slipped through the gaps they poked their heads into the nooses and made a neat job of strangling themselves. Another little dodge I had of pullin' pheasants from their roost was with a snare fixed on a long hazel stick. You got to be pretty smart at that, though, and have good eyes for seein' in the dark. Another thing, and this is specially for you, young 'un, I never wear a white shirt or carry anything white, and I always remember to enter a wood with t'wind blowin' towards me. It's a funny thing, too, that all wild critters will sooner squat down than run, and birds rather run than fly off. I've found I could get within two feet of a crouchin' pheasant provided I never looked him in the eye. Directly you do that, he'll set up a squawk fit to warn every keeper in miles, and away he'll flap."

He stops his slow talk for the moment, while he fills his pipe from my pouch and puffs away contentedly.

Then, as though the thought has just struck him, he says with a twinkle in his eye: " You got to watch out for jays and blackbirds, for they're real varmints for givin' alarm. Pigeons, too, will never fly right over a man, but will suddenly break off in their flight, and make plenty of noise with their flapped-together wings. Ah, but now everything is different, with all these chaps in cars comin' out from t'towns at night. Rare makes a man want t'old days back again."

He shakes his head sadly, but soon cheers up again when we reach home and gather round the cheery fire—for the late evenings soon get very nippy—and we settle down to enjoy our meal with relish.

" Are there any secrets about the way you handle wild creatures? " you ask Peter as we sit round the fire after supper. " Some people seem to be able to do what they like with any bird or animal."

" Now you've touched on a good point there, young 'un," old Peter replies. " You just watch a man who knows a thing or two about horses quieten a horse that has been frighted. He comes up quietly and mutters soothin' words all the while, and when he touches the horse it's not a quick grab but a gentle, soft rub, which takes away all the animal's fear. If you hold any wild critter t'proper way they 'ont struggle. Why, bless me, even a savage mad dog is harmless if you can get hold of him with your knees jest behind his shoulders and so stop him a-goin' backwards or forwards. You've got to hold him with a good grip, too, by the skin around his lower jaw.

" Jest the same wi' holdin' a fox, which is a rare tough job if you don't know how," Peter continues with a chuckle. " You have to grip him by the neck wi' your left hand, gettin' hold of as much skin as you can jest where his neck joins his head, and then wi' your right hand you grip the skin of his back jest above his tail.

" You know t'old sayin' about a cornered rat turnin' on 'ee? Well, best way t'hold one of they critters is by the tip of t'tail, so the weight of his body keeps his head well down, or you can grip him hard from above by t'neck and shoulders so the varmint can't turn on 'ee wi' his teeth. Why, I've handled hundreds of rats this way and nary a bite, but be quick to have summat rubbed on one if you're ever bitten, young 'un, for there's no dirtier critter in his ways than a rat.

" Don't 'ee try to hold a mouse by his tail, though," Peter says, after you have digested this information. " A mouse 'll curl up and give 'ee a rare ol' nip if 'ee do! "

" I remember Toby catching a mouse, and the cheeky little blighter sitting on its haunches and waving its little paws about as much as to say ' come on, then '," I break in laughingly. " Toby looked too amazed at first to try anything, but when he did make a grab he got a bite on the nose which made him jump back pretty smartly. I couldn't help admiring the mouse's pluck, though."

Old Peter rises reluctantly as he glances at the clock above the mantelpiece. " Toime I was a-goin'," he says; " but if 'ee both care to meet oi at the bridge in t'mornin' we'll do a bit of fishin' after jack pike."

" Jolly good idea! " I exclaim, and excitedly you retire for the night, dreaming of the huge pike you *may* land under Peter's expert guidance.

CHAPTER XI

Battles With the River-Wolf

PIKE-FISHING WITH OLD PETER—TRICKS AND TIPS FOR THE FISHERMAN—TALKS ABOUT
FISH—EELS, TENCH, CARP, PERCH, TROUT, AND OTHER WATER-DWELLERS

We are astir early in the morning—which looks as though it will be overcast and dull—and after a hearty breakfast we again make our way to the old mill bridge. In the distance we can see Old Peter, and we give him a hail when we are within shouting distance.

As I know full well, the great beauty of pike-fishing is that at any moment you may hook a real whopper, not a miserly little thing that hardly moves the float, but one that takes the line with a swish and a rush, and which gives you a battle before he is landed.

The pike has been aptly described as the freshwater wolf, and it well deserves its name, being a long, very fearsome-looking fish, with huge mouth and strong jaws, which come together with a click of sharp teeth over an unfortunate victim. It is greenish-brown in general colour, being paler on the sides, and showing a touch of gold and silver on the underparts. It is very widely distributed over the whole of the fresh-water lakes and rivers of the country and has a variety of local names. Old Peter, living in the South, calls it a " jack ", but in the North and in Scotland it is usually referred to as a " gade ".

" Jack " leads a solitary life, as you would suppose from a killer such as he, and among other things that go to form his food are moles, frogs, newts, water-voles, rats, and even young moor-hens. He wages an unending struggle—usually pretty successfully, too—against keepers in spots where game fish are preserved, and his mottled colouring makes him very difficult to spot among the water-weeds of a stream. It is by means of this protective colouring that Jack is able to approach within a few inches of his victim without raising its suspicions.

Pike mate about February, and in very early spring we might have seen a pair together in the spot where Peter knows there is a real " big 'un ". It has recently been discovered that pike go to sea for spawning, and it is then that the river estuaries are full of the fish. The female is much larger than the male, and will lay the almost incredible number of over half a million eggs. In a day or two these rise to the top of the water, and after about fourteen or twenty days hatch out.

Only a few months pass before the young are well able to fend for themselves, and when one has found a feeding-ground which suits its fancy it will guard this jealously and fight desperately any invaders.

It is in the twilight of a summer evening that jack will pay a visit to the shallow waters. There, taking full advantage of its colouring, it catches and devours hundreds of small fish, which are seized in the middle and held crosswise in its jaws for some moments before being swallowed.

Peter, who has caught hundreds of pike in his adventurous career, knows that jack will eat like fury for a few days and then fast, and that really the best time for landing a good catch is in sharp, frosty weather, when their appetites are sharpened.

There are three common forms of pike tackle: the live gorge, spinning and " snapping ". In the first case, a hook is fixed to the bait, and this, Peter reminds us, the jack must be allowed to swallow before the hook can hold. It will grab at the bait, which can be almost anything, roach being the great favourite, hold it crosswise for a moment, then turn it and swallow it headfirst. Then, as the prongs of the hook are pointing to the tail, the bait becomes effectively caught.

" Don't 'ee be in any hurry to go a-pullin' on it in, see? " says Peter

ROACH

firmly. " You must give 'un time to gorge; 'bout ten minutes 'll do, afore you pull 'un in."

You nod, silently excited.

" This mornin' us 'll catch a few roach for bait, and we might have time t'see a few other things as well," Peter continues, and you just look in the basket to make sure you have the bread-paste we shall use as bait for this smaller, brightly coloured fish, which abounds in most rivers.

It is a good plan to combine roach and pike fishing, for although you may sit quietly for hours on the river bank catching the smaller fry, you may have a few hectic moments of sudden excitement if a pike takes a bait you have left out for another line. If there *is* a pike about, the roach will be too scared to eat, so it is a good idea to be prepared. If you want a change from bread-paste for roach bait, then try the freshwater shrimps you can find clinging to the river weeds, ordinary worms, boiled wheat, or caddis-worms. It is a good notion to throw in a ball of bran and bread mixed to act as ground-bait.

" Some jack be as fussy as an old hen about their food," says Peter, as we prepare our lines. " But if he don't take any of our bait then we'll try a frog, if you can find us one around, young 'un. There bain't no better bait to attract him. Y'see, a pike 'll notice and swim after a frog when it's jerkin' about when p'raps he'll pass an or dinaryfish-bait by. I've known a bit of red ribbon tied to a bait to fetch 'im, too.

" Now ' snappin' ' is a different story. You use the same bait, but directly Jack takes the bait you give a real good heave and drive the hooks into his mouth. Sometimes you've got to fish this way, 'cause when Jack's not too hungry he'll just play about with your bait and then leave it, so unless you can snap him up quick as light when he first makes a grab at the bait, then he's away."

Peter ceases his lesson, every word of which you have been following with the utmost intentness, and I butt in with the remark that I think the best sport of any is spinning with a spoon-bait or using natural bait. You have to give wily Jack the idea that his prey is darting away through the water, and in his hurry to make a quick grab he will often take a brightly glittering spinning-bait without thought. This bait is a piece of highly polished metal, something like a handle-less spoon, and turns very quickly as it is drawn through the water, looking just like the gleaming silvery side of a roach.

We have our lines out for roach by now, and in a fairly short time we have caught several of these with our bread-paste.

After a time, however, the nibbles become very rare, and then we sit for some time without any movements of our floats.

" 'Tis a good sign," says Peter solemnly, as he draws at his pipe. " Probable that Jack has scared 'em off. He should be about here by now. I know his little ways." He chuckles to himself, and we watch the gorge-line we have out loosely with quickening interest. Another quiet quarter of an hour passes, when suddenly the gorge-line moves with a rush, and away sings the line.

It is a good hard tussle while it lasts, but Peter's wits are more than a match for the wily pike, and at last we have him, flapping and gleaming, on the bank, a savage, vicious fish who still has plenty of bite in those strong jaws and who needs careful handling as yet.

The catch gives Old Peter a sense of complete satisfaction, and as we tramp home at the hour of midday we fall to talking of other fish which dwell in our streams and rivers, and of their habits.

" I wonder how many times, young 'un, you've seen lots of small, wiry-looking fish, about four inches long and with sharp snouts, when you've been wading, and wondered what they were? You know, at certain times of the year these ' elvers ', as they're called— they're really young eels, y'know—are to be found in thousands coming up-river from the sea. Gulls get as many as they can eat, but still there are enough left to come up-river and develop into fine, big eels."

Peter pauses for a moment, and I take up the story.

" And these elvers, John, are about three years old by the time they reach the rivers from the sea where they were born—in the deep waters of the Atlantic—and when they started their journey they were flat, ribbon-shaped objects with a very small head. They don't travel very far —the first year remaining very deep in the ocean—but by the end of the third year they are about three inches long, and then they change into elvers. While doing this they have to stop feeding, for, curiously enough, they have to grow a new set of teeth!

" But although there were countless numbers of them when they started, many enemies have taken their toll, and in no river or lake will you ever find a shoal of eels. For about seven years eels will live in whatever pond or stream they eventually settle in—then some strange urge makes them start on a journey of thousands of miles, from the quiet waters of an English river to the vast depths of the Atlantic. No one knows how long this journey takes, but we are certain that eventually all the eels *do* reach their own birthplace, amazing as this sounds. It is here that the female lays her eggs, and after they have been fertilized by the male both male and female eels die.

" The journey seems almost as incredible as that of the swallows, which, by the way, I see are gathering well on the wires now in preparation for their long, stormy journey to Africa for the winter. We can understand why the swallows leave us for the winter, for their natural food consists of insects such as gnats, and they would feed pretty badly with us all winter! What we can't understand, though, is why on earth an eel has to travel all those thousands of miles to lay its eggs when it could just as well hatch its young in the quiet waters where it spends most of its life. It's just another of those unsolved mysteries of Nature, I suppose."

We find we have started discussing a topic on which we can talk for a long while, for we have a good many varieties of fish in our rivers.

A common sluggish-water dweller, which I always think tastes very like the mud above which it swims, is the tench. This is rather a heavily built fish, with a clumsy-looking body and blunt head. It also has an almost square tail, and its scales are so small that they are difficult to see at all. Its colouring of dull brownish-green, with touches of bronze-gold on the sides, is just right to give it protection when above mud. It spends most of its life grubbing for worms on the roots of water-weeds in the soft mud, and you will rarely see much of the tench, although there may be a good number about. The female is another terrific egg-layer, like the pike, and will have a " clutch " of over a quarter of a million. Very few of these survive, however, for a good many water-creatures devour them as a delicacy. I suppose about eight pounds is the best weight it attains in England, with a length of some twelve inches.

" Same place as you'll find tench so you'll most likely see carp," says Peter, who knows some good spots where these fish—at one time considered food for the monks—are to be found.

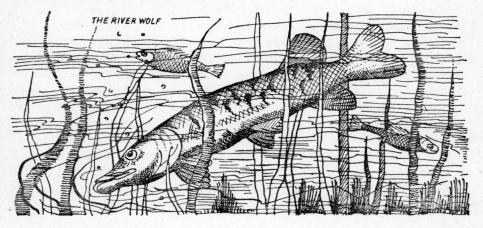

THE RIVER WOLF

They prefer a muddy, reed-grown bottom to a clearer, swift-running stream. The carp is a handsome fish, with a body covered with large brownish-tinted scales, which gleam a dull gold in the sunlight. It is unlike the tench in its habits, for it likes to roll in lazy fashion near the surface of the water, and seems to enjoy the sun. Many legends have grown up around solitary carp, which are solemnly reputed to be " 'undreds o' years " old, but it is a fact that it is one of the quickest-growing of our freshwater fish, and *will* live for perhaps a hundred years in some quiet spot. It can also live for several hours out of water, so you see it hangs on to life pretty grimly! How many fish would stand the treatment it sometimes receives abroad, where, packed in damp moss, it is posted from one place to another, and still flicks a lively tail when placed again in water!

" I think I've heard somewhere that eels will sometimes travel from one pond to another over the ground," you break in at this stage. " Is that possible? "

I had been expecting some question like this, for it was obvious that you were pondering deeply over some problem, and I am able to tell you that eels *do* make such journeys, almost always at night, and while they are still fairly young. When an eel comes on land, liquid held in small, bag-like chambers, which lie over the gills and are filled with water, enables it to breathe by its gills, and as long as this water-supply lasts the eel can survive. The female, by the way, grows much larger than the male, and may reach up to five feet in length and attain a weight of some fifteen pounds.

One of the most handsome as well as most common of our fish is the perch. With its greenish general body colour, and band of black or bluish green along the back, stripes of the same shade on its sides, and gold and bronze patches on its head, it makes a very delightful picture. The tail and the fins on the underparts, also, are bright red.

The perch is a bold little fellow, and enjoys the warmth and light of the sun near the surface of the water. Small fish, frogs, tadpoles, shrimps, worms and water-insects form its food, but it has a black heart despite its gay appearance, and will turn cannibal and swallow any other perch that it can catch. The stiff spines on the fore part of its back fin protect it greatly from attacks by pike, for their sharp points stick in the mouth of the big fellow, and he fights shy of this. At about three years old the perch stops growing and if you are lucky you may catch a big one up to about five pounds in weight.

We mustn't forget that angler's target on so many days, the trout, for this is to be found in all our inland waters, especially in the South, and although never reaching any great weight it makes for good sport. It is a member of the salmon tribe, and loves swift-running, clear streams, shunning any stagnant water. They make what is called a " redd " for the eggs on the gravelly bottom of a stream, and cover these with a deep layer of gravel. During the season of the May-fly, which hatch

SPECKLED TROUT

out in chalky streams and rivers, they leap and jump from the water, gorging themselves until they can take no more. It is then that the clever dry-fly angler has his red-letter days. Trout have a remarkable habit of changing their shades of colour to suit their surroundings, and the chalk-stream dwellers are much clearer and lighter than those in peaty, darker streams.

" You saw how almost transparent were those Peter tickled yesterday? " I exclaim to you, as we near home. " But they still retain their handsome spots, which are a characteristic feature."

Oh, yes, the waters of our English rivers, streams and ponds are a mass of life, some of it so small that it needs a microscope to see it! Then there are stickleback and minnow, both gay little fellows, the stickleback being the only fish which builds a nest of reeds for its eggs. Common and crested newts, dragonflies, water-shrimps, scorpions, frogs and toads, May-flies, water-boatmen—these are but a few of the inhabitants in and over our pools.

An expert in camouflage that is worth looking for is the water-scorpion, for it looks so like a small rotting dead leaf when it is nesting that it takes a keen eye to see it. Dark-brown in colour, it is very flat, and scarcely thicker than the leaves it imitates. It has two pair of walking and swimming legs, long and thin, and these can be folded beneath its body. The front pair are fitted with formidable talons, with which prey is seized. The scorpion then proceeds to suck dry the victim by means of a sharp beak which protrudes between its keen, wicked eyes.

During autumn, the lovely flashing dragonflies are found in great abundance along every river and stream, but as winter draws on the dwellers of the river have to depend on the weather for their way of life.

It is surprising how many water creatures *can* be found in a mild December or January. When the frost and ice is thick, however, down to the mud of the bottom they go, and there they remain dormant and without activity until the cold spell is over.

In all, it makes a wonderful study to follow the life of our water-dwellers throughout the year, and although we may not have Old Peter's great knowledge it doesn't take a great while to pick up a fair intimacy with those creatures, from the wolfish pike to the smallest insect.

SWALLOWS GATHERING

CHAPTER XII

Autumn and " The Eyes of Night "

AUTUMN, AND TEA IN THE TWILIGHT—THE GREAT BIRD MIGRATION—" FOREIGNERS "
OF THE MARSHLANDS—FIELD INVADERS—THE STARS, " EYES OF THE NIGHT "—COUNTRY
WEATHER WISDOM

It is autumn, the fall of the year, when the earth smells mellow and dank after a shower, and the lanes are full of decaying leaves of many hues. It is no time for the caravan, but rather for long walks in early-darkening afternoons, with a welcome tea with toast and scones in the twilight, or hour of dimmity, as it is called in Devon.

As far as the birds are concerned, it is the beginning of the year. Those who stay with us all through the seasons have finished moulting, and those who come for an all-too-short summer visit are preparing to leave for their winter quarters. The opening months of autumn and spring are the really busy times for birds, as far as we are concerned, for in those months—September and October and March and April— more varieties are to be found than at any other time of the year, for these are the great seasons of coming and going.

Many of our birds do not sing after June, and it is difficult to know when they slip away until the following spring. The swallows and martins make themselves heard and seen very much in their final conference on the wires before leaving, and thousands of these handsome little birds will be lining a stretch of telegraph wire one day and will have disappeared completely on the morrow. Most of the other visitors, however, depart without fuss, and are not seen to leave.

I always feel a sense of melancholy in late autumn, due in part to the plaintive little song of the robin, who seems to be the only one with a voice now. His song seems *so* different from the cheerful little snatches he trilled for us as we set off on the spring caravan tour, but there is *very* much to see around us still, and it is a mistake to suppose that we have more birds with us in summertime than winter. In fact, our winter population is certainly greater, for huge numbers of birds that have only to find food for themselves flock to our shores—most of them being water-birds—from the Northern Scandinavian countries, where the weather in the long winter months is much more severe than we experience.

These visitors start arriving before the last of the summer migrants leave us. Shoveller ducks and mallards arrive in large numbers, with wigeon and teal, tufted duck and pochards, to mention a few; and by the end of September the first contingent of the huge flocks of waders has reached our northern and east-coast marshes.

How well I remember the hours spent on the huge marshes, criss-crossed with innumerable channels which filled and emptied with the tide, near St. Oysth, in Essex, where the lonely air has resounded to melancholy long trills and wild calls, which seem to fit into the surroundings. Masses of waders could be seen following the edge of the tide, busily digging out all the water-insects left stranded. One thing I could never understand was how, as though at the command of a leader, a whole flock would suddenly rise and wheel round in a huge circle of swift-moving wings and then settle once more about a mile farther along the coast.

Our lapwing population increases to a great extent now, being added to by flocks of " foreigners ", and I am always pleased to see these, for the amount of good they do on the land by ridding it of grubs can never be fully appreciated. It would be a sad day if the lapwing was seen no more, although a short while ago the numbers did start to decrease badly.

Long-drawn and musical, yet breathing the very spirit of a restless soul, the " pee-a-wit, peee-wit " of a circling flock of lapwings, with their brilliant black-and-white plumage, long curling headfeathers, and coats which glitter with all imaginable colours when caught by the sun, fits in once more with the mood of autumn and winter. Have you ever noticed how birds have calls and songs which are just right for their surroundings? I have never discovered one yet that was out of place.

Along with the lapwings in the autumn-ploughed fields march huge flocks of " phewing " starlings, *the* mimics of the bird world.

In the evening, mass flights of these birds, presenting an almost solid black

MAGPIES

mass
against
the evening
sunset, wheel and
turn over the marshes
before going to roost.

October brings a fresh invasion, and redwings, a thrush-like bird with a spot of red on each wing, and field-fares are about in the fields in flocks. The field-fare has a harsh "chacking" cry which you cannot mistake once you have heard it. Have you noticed, John, how more and more the birds that have been in pairs all summer are now gathering in flocks and hang about the farm more all day? Gold and green finches and chaffinches, yellow-hammers, tits, sparrows, all are seen together in greater numbers now than at any time, and it is a pretty sight to watch a flock of lovely coloured goldfinches working over a teasel patch, swiftly extracting the seeds from the fluffy heads. Then, suddenly, off they will go in a bunch, with a jerking, up-and-down flight and a constant twittering among themselves.

Rooks and jackdaws gather in greater numbers than ever now, and rooks sometimes can be seen flying in a noisy formation back to their evening roosts, cawing and flapping loudly all the time. It is quite dark before they eventually settle down to stillness.

These winter roosts, by the way, John, are not the same as the spring rookeries, which are left alone all winter. But, built with stout twigs as they are, the rookeries withstand the most severe storms, and remain, black as ever, in the topmost branches of the elms until February brings activity back to them once more.

Often now we may see quite large gatherings of magpies, splendid in pure black-and-white, with long, fan-spread tails, and these make a fine sight against the dying foliage.

Towards late evening is the time I like best, though. Then, after a fine autumn day, pigeons fly in to roost in hundreds in every coppice, blackbirds and jays seem to scream alarm calls all the time, and pheasants keep up a steady " cock-up, cock-up " until they, too, eventually settle to roost on the lower branches of trees in the game-woods.

Then above us twinkle the countless points of light we call stars, and on this fine still and very clear evening, John, I suggest we try to discover a little about hese far-off planets.

" ' The man-in-tne-moon ' is well out tonight, Woodman," you exclaim, as we stand taking deep breaths of the pine-scented air, and watching the outlines of the firs and larches swaying and sighing gently in the quiet air.

" Yes, John, and under a telescope it is shown that the friendly face ' we all know becomes vast plains and mountain-ranges. It is the light reflected from the sun that causes the shadows that give the appearance of a face. The dark areas, which are fairly free from craters, are called ' seas ' or ' ocean beds ', but there is probably no water on the moon. There doesn't appear to be any atmosphere as we know it, either, and with no clouds the moon appears to be a dead world. Probably if man ever does get there, John, in a space-ship, he will be jolly glad to turn round and come back—if he *could* get back—for there is almost certain to be no life or vegetation as we know them. It seems that the moon certainly will never offer holiday attractions, at any rate!

" The sun, moon and other planets all follow a wandering course across the sky, but all around these are the smaller stars, and it is impossible for us to grasp the vastness of the distance which separates them. Strangely enough, light from the sun reaches us in just over eight minutes, despite the huge distance it has to come, but light from the Pole Star, which has been used to guide sailors and adventurers across unchartered seas and continents since the dawn of time, takes five hundred years. Just think, John, that the light from the Pole Star we can see tonight started from the star in Henry VI's reign! Amazing, isn't it?

" Despite all the complicated movements the earth and other planets constantly perform, the Pole Star remains a wonderful guide, for its direction is always very nearly true north. Now just look at that large

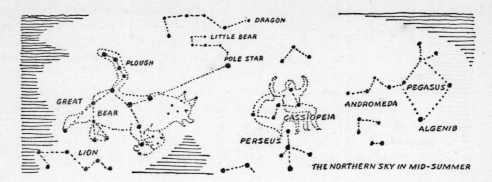

THE NORTHERN SKY IN MID-SUMMER

group of seven bright stars up there known as the Plough. The last two stars act as pointers to the Pole Star, and if you follow these through you will see, quite a good distance away, the North Star. The distance between the last 'pointer' and the Pole Star is about five times that between the two pointers themselves, so this will help you to locate it."

" It isn't a very bright star, though, is it, Woodman? " you exclaim, when we have found our star. " I would have thought it would have been the brightest of the lot."

" No, it certainly isn't as bright as the stars of the Plough, John, but there are many degrees of brightness among stars. In ancient times the various stars were divided up into groups, and the name of some mythical figure given to each group. The Plough, now, forms part of the Great Bear, while the Pole Star comes in the Little Bear group.

" The grandest of all the groups is Orion, the Hunter. These brilliant stars rise in the east and set in the west, and during the autumn and winter Orion is always to be seen in the southern part of the sky. The stars form a large cross, and in the centre are three closely grouped stars which are supposed to be the belt of the Hunter. Hanging like a sword from this belt is a line of stars, and the whole group *can* be placed together to form the rough figure of Orion.

" There are many, many such groups, all worthy of a detailed study, but one interesting happening that is taking place at this moment is worth our attention. Across the sky wings a swift trailing blaze of light, and then all is dark again. It was what we call a ' shooting star ', and was probably a mass of stone from some planet. In its flight through space it became white-hot by the friction of our atmosphere, and thus gave off an intense light. Very few of these stone masses reach the earth —thank goodness!—but those that do are called meteorites, and have

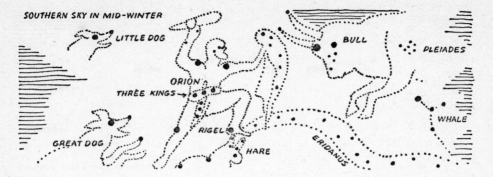

SOUTHERN SKY IN MID-WINTER · LITTLE DOG · BULL · PLEIADES · ORION · THREE KINGS → · WHALE · GREAT DOG · RIGEL · HARE · ERIDANUS

been found in all parts of the world. Some have weighed several tons.

"One of the things that has been the cause of more downright 'cussin'' in every part of our tight little island is the uncertainty of our weather, and even the radio broadcasts are listened to without any real belief, for no man seems able to predict just what the weather *will* be in a few hours' time. I would rather rely on Old Peter than any radio myself, for it is uncanny how birds, animals, and those who spend their lives among them, are easily the finest weather-prophets.

"What was Old Peter saying last evening, John?" I continue, as we gaze at the sky. "I think some of his sayings and his wisdom are really extraordinary. What about the other day, when it was drizzling so badly? Yet he said it would clear up in a short while. It certainly looked as though it would rain all day, but he was right, and shortly afterwards the sun was actually shining. The radio, too, had predicted rain, so he had no help there!

"Remember that we asked him how he did it when we got home again, and do you remember his reply? It was one of those things that should be written in the notebook for future guidance. It went something like this: 'Well, marster, just afore you come along I were a-watchin' they cattle over there. There they were, all a-lyin' down and chewin' the cud as quiet as you could wish. Now if they'd been standin' up restless-like, then we could 've been certain of a wet day, but when you see 'em lyin' down you can be sure fine weather is on the way pretty soon.' Another thing Peter told us was that whenever cattle and sheep are restless and noisy then you can expect rain, and if in dull weather you see rabbits feeding away from their warrens in daylight then look out for a wet, stormy night! There is no creature which hates to get his fur wet more than friend rabbit, and he knows, with some uncanny instinct that all wild creatures seem to possess, that he must feed early or spend a hungry night."

Just at this moment we see a tall, stooping figure, carrying a sack slung over his shoulder, approaching us, and sure enough it *is* Old Peter.

"Hullo there, Peter!" I cry. "We were just talking about you. Were those old ears of yours red?"

Peter chuckles and puts down his sack. We do not ask what it contains, but we can make a good guess! We fall once more to discussing weather prophecies, and Peter, who is always in his glory at this form of nature-craft, gives us a few more of his many grains of long-garnered knowledge.

"'Tis a good plan to see what the rooks are a-doin' early mornings. If they be busy feeding in the fields mebbe a mile or so from the rookery 'tis sure we'll have a fine day. 'Tis when they hang about close to the elms all the time that you got to look out for storms.

"On a really foggy, damp, autumn mornin' 'tis a very good sign if you can see the dew a-glitterin' on the spiders' webs which seem to cover pretty near every inch of the fields and hedges. You can rely on a good hot day when you see this. Now take tonight, for instance. Why, bless me, you'd say with all them stars you can see so clear that tomorrow would sure to be a fine day, but just you mark my words and see if you don't need your coats in the mornin'."

"My word, Peter, you're a cheerful one," you say gloomily. "Fancy telling us a thing like that! I would never have thought that seeing all those stars so clearly meant rain."

"Ah, young 'un, there's many a thing you don't know as yet. I've seen you carryin' round a little notebook, haven't I? Well, here's a few more old saws you can put in it. When the evenings are red and the next morning grey, you'll get a fine day. When you hear cocks a-crowin' afore you go to bed then look out for a wet day. I suppose you know the old one about a rainbow at night bein' the shepherd's delight, and a rainbow in the mornin' bein' the shepherd's warnin'? And watch out if you see deep reddy-coloured clouds at sunrise or sunset. This is a sure sign of storms and gales.

"I s'pose you've heard lots of townfolk who think they know a thing or two about the weather say that a good big crop of hips and haws and other berries like we're havin' this year is a sure sign that we're in for a hard winter? But don't you believe it, young 'un, for it only goes to show that the spring and summer has been just right for their growth. Why, I remember in some of the mildest winters I've known seein' masses of berries everywhere in autumn. If we get a good crop of beech mast, now, you can expect to see plenty of pigeons about, for they like these more than anythin'."

We continue our walk in the clear night air, and leave Old Peter to his activities, about which we do not say much in his hearing.

" What I'd like to know, Woodman, is what anti-cyclone and depression mean. I'm always hearing these on the wireless."

" Well, you see, John, between Iceland and Greenland there is a cold current flowing from the north-east, with winds from the same direction. Another cold current moving south-eastward meets this, and in this region there is a terrific disturbance, or what is popularly called 'a depression'. This can be anything up to a thousand miles across and usually means bad weather, but when the path of this depression goes over Iceland we usually have a spell of good weather.

" Now anti-cyclone means just the opposite of depression, with light winds and high-pressure periods, which move very slowly or remain quite motionless for several days. In summer this means dry, cloudless days with very misty evenings and hot sun. In winter, however, an anti-cyclone brings frost and fog or grey overcast skies.

" November used to be called ' wind-monath ', or month of the wind, by the Anglo-Saxons, and it was then that the fishermen drew in their boats high on the shore and stacked away their nets until the following spring.

" But still, despite all its uncertainty, I really don't think that you would find any countryman who would really want to alter our climate, for it is one that usually allows us to attend the harvest-festival service in our local church thankful for still yet another fine crop from the good English earth."

STORM CLOUDS

The one period of the year perhaps when there is more interest taken in the country, even by the most ardent town-lover, is at harvest, for haven't you always felt a queer thrill as you went into church in the evening for the harvest-festival service, and found the interior filled with the multicoloured fruits of the soil? Wheat, marrows, swedes, carrots, beetroot, barley, long loaves, and produce of every description, is brought to the church for this special occasion each year, and even now, when so many of our old country customs are being allowed to die out, this service is still maintained.

There is always an overpowering smell of the " good earth " from this produce, and you know, John, there is always a deeper pride in the singing of the hymns. Every day has brought its troubles and many worries to the farmers, for we are lucky if we ever get two days alike in weather, as we have found out on our tours. But somehow, despite all the head-shaking and murmurings that always go on among countrymen everywhere, the harvest of the fields is gathered in every autumn—a harvest that it would be impossible to live without, and you know how every one of us had to grow as much as we possibly could during the long years of the war, John, when you spent many of your holidays helping on the land.

But, of course, most of the romance has gone out of farming today. The smelly tractor is replacing the old, sturdy horses, and it is only rarely that villagers observe the old customs that were once such a feature of country life. At one time the horses were always festooned with garlands of flowers, and sunflowers and ribbons were fixed to their blinkers, when they brought in the last load of wheat. On the leading horse, too, was always seated the prettiest girl on the farm, and my old grandmother, now a mass of wrinkles, delights in telling me still how she was picked many times for this honour. She was always dressed in white and had flowers in her straw hat, and a yellow sash. And then over the wagon was always placed a corn baby. This was made from a single sheaf of the best corn, and resembled a human shape, dressed with paper clothes and wearing a paper hat.

Then there was a procession through the village of all the workers, heading which was the village band. No, John, no one was ever very critical of the musicians. For a whole week everyone set out to enjoy themselves; the fun was fast, and the cider and beer free-flowing. As the leading cart entered the farmyard from the fields, it was the custom of my grandfather, so says grandmother, to leap upon the shafts and shout:

" We have ploughed, we have sowed,
      We have reaped, we have mowed,
      We have brought home every load,
      Hip, hip, hip, Harvest Home! "

The whole crowd of workers would join in shouting the last two words, and then the large wheat-cakes and home-brewed beer were handed round. After the men and women had put on their best suits and long dresses, and carefully plastered down their hair, polished their Sunday boots, and taken the paper " crackers " from their hair, the whole party gathered again for an evening's fun and dancing. The fiddler was always a popular person at this time, for where were they without his cheerful, piping music? The little, spindly-legged old fellows who trudged around the countryside month in and month out earned many a penny at Harvest Home. They were always welcome in the villages, too, on account of the lack of newspapers, for they and the travelling tinkers and carriers were the news-bringers of the day, and as the housewife bargained over the purchase of a piece of cloth from the pedlar who called about every three months, she would learn all the gossip he had picked up in his travels.

But come, John, I was forgetting to tell you of the wonderful supper that always followed the dancing. Grandmother makes my mouth water even now when she tells me how, all class distinction forgotten, the whole company sat down to the good old English roast beef and plum pudding, with once more the cider and beer barrels being emptied. Then would follow toasts to the farmer and his wife, to the good earth, the plough, the sickle and the flails, and then—for the countryman was always a religious man, John—they would thank the God who had made another harvest possible.

After this, the farmer would give gifts of money and tobacco to his men and pieces of lace to the women; and, John, as the harvest moon rose slowly and lit the countryside with a deep yellow light, the company of men and women of the land would sing the old country songs that had been handed down to them during the years. Grandmother always has two tears trickling down her wrinkled cheeks as she tells me this, and perhaps I have had too, for although we two are finding something of the England of green fields in our travels, there is a spirit of the soil that seems to have gone forever.

CHAPTER XIII

Autumn Round the Camp-Fire

OUTDOOR FIRE-MAKING—BOILING THE BILLY—COBHOUSE, INDIAN AND OTHER FIRES—A
TRUDGE THROUGH AUTUMN WOODS—TOADSTOOLS AND MUSHROOMS—TRACKING BROCK
THE BADGER—BROCK AT HOME

It is splendid sitting here with our backs against two fir-trees in the cool of an autumn evening, watching the faint curl of whitish smoke rising dreamily from our small fire. Against the roundness of the moon the delicate tracery of the firs stands out in black relief. It is the time to listen to the bubble of the boiling water in the billycan and at the same time keep an ear open for noises of the prowlers of the night.

Is there any better friend or more cheerful companion than the crackling log fire? But here, as in so many other things in the outdoor life, you must first learn the art of making a fire that will enable you to pass as a real woodman, and not just a town-dweller making a bonfire!

The best way to boil a small billy of water, as I have found, is to cut a short forked stick, sharpen the thicker end, and leave the fork at the top. Drive this firmly into the ground, and then take a longer stick that still has plenty of sap in it and cut a notch at one end. Then sharpen the other end, and drive this into the ground so that the long part of the stick is held well above the ground by resting in the fork of our first, short stick. Hang the billy from the notch of this green stick, which will bend with its weight until it swings above the fire at the height you require. Now to build our little fire—and " little " is the right word, by the way, for there is nothing that condemns an amateur fire-lighter more than a huge mass of wood.

For the centre of the fire you need a small heap of dry leaves, pine-needles, grass, or shavings from a dry twig. Around this, set some very small dry twigs—about as thick as knitting needles—in the shape of a pyramid, and leave plenty of gaps for air. Over these place larger twigs until you have a neat little wig-wam shape, not more than a few inches across or high. Then just light the centre of this and soon, with a little sensible feeding of heavier twigs, you will have a glowing fire that will boil the billy in next to no time.

Another good fire is called the cobhouse. For this, you arrange four stout sticks to form a square on the ground. In the centre of this you place your shavings and small twigs, and then make a criss-cross pattern with more twigs on the first four. Build this up until you have a skeleton erection that allows the draught to sweep clear between the twigs. This roars away well and soon gives you some hot ashes.

The Indians, those wonderful masters of the woodcraft trail, never wasted their labour, and one of their favourite fire methods was to lay three or four good sized twigs or small logs on the ground like the spokes of a wheel. The ends of these formed a small circle in the centre, and in this a small fire was started. Then, when the larger logs burnt through at the ends, they were just given a push inwards from time to time. I have always found this to be one of the best means of making the type of fire that you can sit round all evening without having to be constantly putting on fresh logs. I have even kept one going all night by just pushing the logs farther in each time I stirred during the long dark hours. It is a pretty cheering thing, too, to find your fire still alight in the still hours of the early dawn, and it is then that the boiling billy always seems to me to be the sweetest music of first light. It even rivals the lovely liquid notes of the thrush and blackbird!

If you have to cook for several people, however, it is best to lay your fire between two lines of bricks or stones. Notice which way the wind is blowing first, and then spread your bricks out so that the draught blows down your tunnel and the smoke is driven through the narrow end. Whether you use this method or dig a narrow trench over which you can place an iron bar or two, the dixies have something firm to rest upon. Whatever you do, never try to balance your dixies or billy right on the burning twigs—it's simply asking for a tipped-up billy when the twigs burn through.

Ah, now we know how best to *make* our fire, but which woods are the best to use? A hard, solid wood, such as oak or ash, gives you a good, slow-burning fire which will leave good red, smokeless embers and last for a long time. Soft woods, however, flare up quickly, and then

MUSHROOMS

are out in a few minutes. This is because they have a good deal of fat or resin in them, which makes them burn easily, but if you use only this you certainly won't be able to lean back against the tree-trunk for long!

A wood that can be burnt green because it is so dry is ash, which is almost the best fuel for a camp-fire. There is an old country rhyme which goes:

Burn ashwood green; 'tis fit for a queen.
Burn ashwood sere, 'twill make a man swear.

This is a very useful thing to remember, for it is a great thing to be able to burn wood that is freshly cut. It does not light up very easily, however, but once you have fair-sized logs going they burn with a clear hot flame and leave some good embers.

One of the most "woodcrafty" woods to use is pine, which has a delightful smell. It gives off a good clear flame, but unfortunately burns fairly fast. Spruce and larch also burn much too quickly. Although the elm is our most common tree, it is pretty near useless on the camp-fire; it just smoulders away, giving out a great deal of smoke and very little heat. Beechwood, on the other hand, is splendid for a good, lasting fire.

One of the most important things to remember when leaving camp is to remove all traces of your fire, and make certain that the embers are thoroughly soaked with water. It is a good idea to cut away sods of turf from the ground on which you will be building your fire and then replace these when you leave.

I wonder if you know the best plan for lighting a fire on a windy day? I find it best to face the wind and light my match inside my cupped hands. Then I strike it so that the head is pointing *towards* the wind. You see why? Well, it's ten to one that the flame will run up the match-stick and keep alight, whereas if you had the head of the match pointing away from the wind it is blown out as soon as you light it.

It is very damp as we trudge through the woods on this late autumn afternoon, and already it is getting quite dusk and chilly. Hazel-nuts and rose-hips fill our haversacks, for much as we like the first as food the hips when crushed and boiled make really fine healthy syrup.

It is " of mice and men and many things " that we have been talking, but mostly of toadstools and mushrooms, for the wood is full of toad-stools of almost every bright colour. It is amazing how very few toad-stools *are* poisonous, and those which are we can quickly recognize. Abroad I have found that a great many varieties of toadstools are eaten, but I am not suggesting that we collect just the first ones we find and fry them over the fire for supper! No; just let's have a look at a few and see which we really *must* leave alone.

The fungus that we call the " toadstool ", which we see in the autumn, is the part on which is produced the spores or tiny " seeds ". These are blown away by the wind, and settle to grow into a new plant. These plants live and grow all the year round, either in soil or in tree-crevices or under rotting logs. The toadstools we usually find consist of a plate-like or cone-shaped cup, usually pretty unhealthy-looking, on a stout stem. The stem is generally provided with a ring about half-way up, and this is quite a guide in identifying the fungus. Now, you know that a mushroom is provided with a large number of gills, like the ribs of an umbrella? Well, many toadstools have gills very similar to the mush-room. It is upon these gills that the spores are produced, but others produce their spores in minute pores running into the surface of the cap.

Anyway, John, I'll try not to be too technical; but just come over here a minute and look at this scarlet flycap. It makes a real splash of scarlet colour among all this autumn dampness, doesn't it? It's one of our most handsome toad-stools. Just notice how thick and white the stem is and that it has a pronounced ring. Those scattered white scales all over the scarlet show up well, too, don't they, and altogether it's quite a villainous - looking

TOADSTOOLS

object. It *is* too, for it is extremely poisonous, and I don't think we will handle it. Do you know that flies and other insects used to be killed by poison extracted from this toadstool?

Here's a scarlet hood over here, too, but this one, although it is as brilliant as our flycap, is *not* poisonous. You can see that it has a quite flat cap only about two inches across. Also the stem is pale-yellow, with a few streaks of red, and has no collar.

" What is the use of those huge white puff-balls, Woodman? " you ask, as you give one of these queer specimens a hearty kick, causing a cloud of white powdery stuff to burst around you.

" Well, John, I hardly know whether it serves any useful purpose, but you have just released thousands of spores, which are held inside the ball until it ripens and bursts. It's possible to make an ink from the black fluid that the maned inkcap toadstools dissolve into after a few hours. You'll have to try it some evening, John. I think you will know this fungus quite well. Remember how we saw thick clusters of light-brownish, thin, spindly-stemmed 'stools in the farmyard this afternoon when we started out? Well, I imagine that by the time we get home again those caps will be black and practically gone, for this will be the spores ripening—it only takes a few hours—and gradually dissolving the caps as they are blown away.

" Look up there—growing out of that old elm, John! That's the striped stump flap—oh, I know these names are all quite a mouthful, but just jot them down in the notebook, and try to make a rough sketch. See how it grows in bracket-like layers from that rotting branch! It is one of our commonest and yet most striking 'stools. Notice how it has various colours, pale-buff on the edges, with dark-green, brown and orange patches. It's quite white underneath, though, and that's where the pores are."

We plod on further, disturbing a flight of pigeons, which sheer off in swift alarm at our appearance.

On a fallen log is a mass of large, semicircular and bracket-like flat caps, and these belong to the giant tuft, the largest of our bracket fungi. These have no stems, but often you can come across some with brownish-yellow caps overlapping to form a group some two feet across.

" I think you know *that* specimen, don't you, John? " I say as I kick over an offensive-smelling, olive-green mass on a thick white stem.

Flies and bluebottles settle on this stinkhorn, as it is called, and after they have eaten the sweetish spores they carry more of these off on their feet and so spread the fungus.

Just let us run over the main features of our friend, the mushroom, which smells so delicious when in the frying-pan. A good maxim always to remember is, "better to be safe than sorry", so it as well to know what to look for. First, there is always a collar round the stem of a 'room. Youngsters—those firm little "buttons"—have pink gills, but these soon turn a purplish colour. They are never really black, however. There is always a space between the gills and the stalk, too, and the skin can be very easily peeled off in flakes. The real 'room always has a pleasant, earthy smell, whereas many of the toadstools have just the opposite odour!

"Wait a minute, John! I believe we have struck a good find today, here. See this deep five-toed print in the soft earth here? It's the mark of a badger. I thought there were some around here somewhere, and if we can track this one down we should see something of interest, even if it's only Brock's front door!"

We search long and diligently for the trail of the pads, and eventually we trace these to a large hole in the corner of a sandy bank, around which the earth is padded smooth by being much used. From the entrance comes the musty odour of a badger.

As we walk home in the gathering darkness we talk much of the badger, one of the *real* creatures of the night, and of its life, all the while planning to spend a night in hiding outside Brock's " sett " in the hope of catching a glimpse of this bear-like wanderer.

It is generally thought, even by people who live in the heart of the country, that the badger is a rare animal, but this is not really

BADGERS

BADGER AT "SETT"

so, and it is fairly widely scattered, especially in the south of England, all over the country. It is because Brock is such a real lover of the cloak of darkness that he is not often seen, except by those whose ways take them to lonely places at night. He keeps well clear of man, too, and as he is quite a silent animal it is little to be wondered at that a man might have had generations of badgers rearing their young in the field next to his country garden plot, and never have seen one.

Brock keeps to his own worn paths and routes, and these will be used for generations. One peculiar habit he has is to sit down every now and then on his trail, and it does not matter how far he goes abroad the faint scent he leaves each time he rests will guide him back to the sett.

Brock is so fussy when it comes to the cleanliness of his deep, underground home that he would please any housewife! Around the sett we have just discovered was a mass of discarded hay, straw and dried leaves, thrown out when fresh bedding was taken down to the sleeping quarters. Brock will even go to the trouble of making his own hay in spring, gathering ferns, grass and leaves, and drying them well in the sun before using them as a soft bed for the soon-to-arrive cubs.

Badgers, like foxes, make first-class parents, and the blind, helpless cubs, born in February or March, are given every attention. There are only two or three of them, as a rule, and they are fed well on a diet of mice, voles, grubs, young rabbits and perhaps a bird or two that has somehow been caught by the slow-moving parents.

It is a curious thing, however, that Brock can live next door, as it were, to a poultry-farm and yet cause very little damage. Oh, yes, he likes an occasional fowl, but he never kills for the sheer lust of killing—as sometimes does a fox—and as he ambles about the countryside at night he is a peaceable enough animal, and just seems to want to be left alone. He keeps an eye open for the approach of dawn, however, for he hates to be caught out after sunrise.

Just as the vixen gives that fearful scream we have heard at night in the woods to attract the dog-fox, so does Brock utter a bloodcurdling yell at this important period, which I have usually found to be in autumn. Perhaps we shall be fortunate enough to hear some of these cries tonight, and here again the cry of the badger at the mating season has frightened many people and been the innocent cause of many a tale of haunting.

During the long winter months Brock is a sensible animal in his habits. About this time of the year badgers get very fat, and their grey coats swell out with the food they consume. Then they see that their deep sleeping quarters are well lined with new bedding, and during long, hard, cold spells they spend many days asleep. They do not hibernate completely, though, and I have often seen fresh pad-marks in snow.

If we try to see Brock this evening we shall have to be very careful not to speak, cough, or snap any twigs as we approach the sett, for the slightest noise will frighten the badger into keeping underground, and we shall not see his queer white face, which has a long black streak from his ears nearly to his nose. He also has white tips to his ears. Brock has a lovely smooth coat, which he keeps brushed by constant rubbing on a favourite stump, to retain its silver-grey sheen. He has the bear-like habit of standing on his hind legs and sharpening his claws on a tree-trunk, and he is fond of wild bee honey! No matter how the bees buzz and storm with rage, Brock absolutely ignores them when he finds a nest, and doesn't leave until he has licked up all the sweet sticky honey he can dig out.

Altogether Brock is a delightful and faithful animal, little seen, but well worth our trouble to try to watch in the dark hours of the night.

Other small creatures of the night hours, seldom seen but often located by their high-pitched squeaks, are the short-tailed meadow-mice, and, believe me, one has to be a clever countryman ever to catch one of these little sharp-eyed, destructive villains!

w-w-w—8

There is no really effective bait for these mice, but over one thousand years ago in a Greek paper the following recipe appeared: "Apuleius suggests smearing the seed with ox-gall and the mice will not touch it, but it is better to get some hemlock seed in the dog-days, and mince it up with hellebore and meal, or to mince together wild cucumber, or henbane,

SHORT-TAILED MEADOW MOUSE

or bitter almond, and black hellebore; mix it with equal parts of meal, make a paste of it with oils and put it in their holes. Tasting, they die. In Bithynia, practical farmers stop their holes with rhododendron leaves, so that the mice, rushing out of the holes, seize the leaves with their teeth. Seizing, they perish." Then the writer adds this very amusing—at least to our minds—piece of advice, which you can follow if you like, John!

"Take paper and write as follows—' I adjure you mice that are found here do me no harm, nor suffer another mouse to do me harm, for I give you this field (here insert details of the field). If I catch any of you here after this, when I get you, by the Mother of the Gods, I will cut each of you into seven parts!' When you have written this, glue the paper, before sunrise, to some stone where the mice are, and be sure that the writing faces outwards. I have included this in case it might appear that I have left anything out. I don't accept anything of this kind, myself Heaven forbid! And I recommend anyone who does not wish to be made a fool of to follow my example."

Just fancy Fred Stokes trying to get rid of mice from his fields by writing them notes! It does seem rather absurd to us now, doesn't it, John, but even in the plague of 1892 in Thessaly all sorts of superstitious remedies were adopted, as they still are in many country districts even now to ward off illness or approaching death. There can always be found the old woman who talks, even gloatingly, of the " death rook ", when a solitary rook circles round and settles on the chimney-stack. "There'll be a death here within a few weeks," is the cheerful message she croaks out! Yes, John, every little creature that is connected with the night has had stories woven round it from the time when there were no books or papers, and the sole entertainment in the long evenings was the inventing and telling of stories that were handed down from one generation to another—with suitable additions, as you can imagine!

But to get back to the meadow-mouse. You know, it is a good thing that there are plenty of enemies of these little beggars, for if there were not they would spread at a fearful rate. You have only to take such a quick-breeding mouse, with a simple taste in vegetable food, strongly inclined to feed under cover, and with small desire to roam far afield, and you can see that it only needs a good quantity of food and cover to allow him to breed and multiply at an amazing rate and gradually spread over a wide area. He is only checked when there is no cover, and that is where the owls and other hunters step in and keep the numbers within reasonable limits.

In nest-building, the meadow-mice construct the soft lining of their homes by biting grass-stems into very short lengths of less than an inch. These they soften by pulling them between their teeth, and as the grass splits apart in this process they soon have a pile of this soft lining material. It is quite easy to follow the runs from a nest, as these are made just below surface-level and the grass above becomes arched and quite distinctive. I have often run two fingers along such a run until it led right back to the hedgerow from perhaps about twenty yards into the field.

The teeth of the meadow-mouse are wonderfully adapted for its life among marshy vegetation. Their surface presents a zigzag set of rough triangles, and when the mouse is busy eating the teeth have the effect of a mincing and grinding machine combined. This is just ideal for the rough and tough marshy plants.

Just another point, John. If you examine the coat of a short-tailed meadow-mouse, you will find it can throw off water, being naturally oily and being composed of very fine hairs set closely together. Altogether like the host of other creatures about which we are slowly learning, the meadow-mouse—like Brock, little seen but there all the same—has been provided by Nature with all that it needs for its way of life.

CHAPTER XIV

Tracking in the Winter Wilds

Like a great mass of soft downy goose-feathers, the snow has been falling for the past two days. Quietly it has blotted out every familiar landmark, and now the white blanket lies deep. The host of small birds we have watched through spring, summer and fall huddle in every tree crack and hollow, under every deep eve of thatched cottage and barn, in their efforts to keep alive during the long cold nights. They puff out their feathers so that the air can circulate and grow warm before it reaches their tiny bodies, but every day when the weather is very severe thousands lie stiff and cold when the pale, watery sun shows in the east once more. It is a hard, bitter struggle for birds and beasts, this fight with the cold of winter, and when snow lies deep on ground and bush then their food situation grows desperate.

Then we can help by supplying all the scraps we can possibly spare, and placing them on a bird-table above the ground, out of the reach of cats. It is really amazing how the same birds that have been so wary of our approach during our recent trips will come to within a few feet of the house in their search for food, and once they lose their first fear of a trap they will grow bolder each day.

You and I can both learn a tremendous amount of interesting details at close range in this way, John, but there is one other phase of winter that I find the most fascinating of all: this is piecing together the story that lies behind the padmarks and the flurry of confused tracks in the snow. There is a thrill in trying to fathom out just what animal or bird made these tracks, and of the fierce, deadly drama that took place when they end in a sudden commotion and a smatter of scattered snow.

Perhaps a few pieces of fur or a feather or two will help us in our work, too. Many are the tracks of rabbit, fox, badger, stoat, rat, mouse, water-fowl, and others, I have followed in mid-winter, and I think that today, John, we will visit the copse, now black and naked against the grey, snow-filled sky, and see if we can read some of these stories behind the trail.

First of all, though, I think we might start with a little study of the trail left by Toby just now, when he dashed away yelping his head off at that black cat.

Toby makes a harder, more untidy trail than the cat, and his foot-prints do not fit one over the other. He also drags his toes.

It looks as though the cat was running on two legs, doesn't it, so perfectly do the rear feet fall into the tracks of the front? It would be difficult to find a more perfect example of tracking grace than the cat displays. When a cat trails a bird or mouse it needs every ounce of concentration on the job, for neither the bird nor the mouse is slow to get off the mark! It cannot choose a safe spot for each hind leg in turn, for even the faintest crackle of a leaf or twig would give the alarm. So, automatically, the cat, after choosing the spots for its front paws, places the rear paws dead into these tracks. This is one of the ways that Nature provides for animals that have to hunt others for their existence.

I really think that even the newest amateur could recognise the trail left by friend rabbit as it bounds along. Its feet make a peculiar pattern, the forefeet being much smaller and touching the ground one in front

FORE REAR
FEET FEET

'JUST AMBLING ALONG'

RABBIT GALLOPING

of the other, while the larger hindfeet make two large marks, side by side, well in front of the forefeet. When a rabbit gallops along, it alternately folds right up and then extends out like a caterpillar. The greater hurry it is in, the greater is the distance between the footprints, so that is a good guide as to its speed. If it is just ambling along quietly, the marks are close together, and the hindfeet no longer reach ahead of the fore-feet.

The trail of the hare, which normally leads such a solitary life, is similar to that of the rabbit, but the prints are larger, and the distance between each set of marks will be greater, for a hare covers a great distance at each bound.

It's a red-letter day when you can learn to read the story of a fox's trail in the snow. This red-coated hunter has the supple paw of a cat, but the dog-like claws show up well. The trail is very narrow, the feet being set nearly in a straight line. The hind pad is smaller than a dog's, however, when you compare the size of the toes. Also, if you look closely, you will see that the foot was a furry one, and whereas the fox has hair between its pads most dogs have only a very little. You will *not* find Reynard stalking boldly along paths used by man, for it avoids these and uses its own roadways across the fields. Look carefully along furrows of autumn-ploughed fields, holes in the bottoms of hedges, and if you manage to spot alongside the prints a red hair or two it will help to tell you that you are on the right track. A point to remember, however, is that the pads of the fox spread very wide on soft soil, and the whole print then looks much larger. If you can find a track leading from firm ground to where Reynard has sprung at a water-hen in the soft mud of the river edge you will see the difference in the size of the track clearly. If, in snow, you can see every now and then long sweeping marks left by the bushy tail, you will have an added check.

A trail that maybe you will find with luck after a night-fall of snow is the five-toed print of our friend of the wood, the badger, that most bear-like of all our creatures of the night. I forgot to tell you before, John, that although it is such a shy creature the young badger is a fluffy bundle of fun-loving mischief, and it is a real joy to watch a family at play on a moonlit evening. Try to watch one of these trails after rain or snow, and you will see the huge hind pad and the unusual five toes, whereas the cat, fox and dog have only four. Maybe you will not always see the fifth toe, but the footprint itself is unmistakable, for the four main toes do not spread out, but are arranged almost in a line. The claws of the forefeet, too, make deep scratches in the soil, and a badger loves to stand on his hind feet and scratch and sharpen his claws on a tree-trunk; so watch for these marks. Brock, as we have already seen, takes a keen delight in rooting out wasps and bumblebees' nests for their sweet-tasting honey, and if you find a mass of broken cells you can bet the badger has had a meal.

On our travels in summer, we often caught a quick glimpse of that

ON FIRM GROUND   FOX   SPLAYED OUT IN MUD

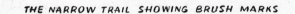

THE NARROW TRAIL SHOWING BRUSH MARKS

sandy-coated little killer, the stoat, but its tracks are likely to puzzle us for a bit, for although it has a small, five-toed track we usually only see four toes in the forefeet prints.

Like a tiny, outspread hand is the track left by the brown rat, and if you are around a stack or barn on a snowy morning there are sure to be thousands about, crossing and recrossing. It is slender-toed; the fore-foot is thumbless, but the hind foot has five toes.

Of a similar nature, but of course smaller, is the trail of the long-tailed fieldmouse, who leaves a most delicate little footprint in the soft earth or mud. Watch for it in snow, and you will see that it hops along in a series of rat-like bounds, and at the end of each leap it strikes the ground with its tail, leaving a long streak in the snow between the marks of the feet.

Perhaps you are lucky enough to live near a stream or river in which a pair of otters have their home, and, if you are, look for the marks of this immensely strong, tailed fisherman on the sandbanks and mud. The otter leaves a round, five-toed track, which, if you look carefully, has traces of the webbing of a water-dweller between the toes. If you find a trout's head and a few scales by the marks you can be doubly certain that there the otter has fed.

Every animal and bird has its own track-marks, and studying them and trying to hunt down the owner improves your knowledge of every form of wild life. Make rough sketches of each track, and jot down the distance between the prints. Note down the general surroundings, see whether any hairs are left, and look all around in a real detective fashion. It's a grand way to sharpen your wits!

Winter in England can be such a mass of contrasts, as we are finding out: sharp, clear, frosty days, when the earth is like concrete; dull, foggy, " muggy " days; days when the wind shrieks and howls with the fury of departed spirits, when to be abroad at night is to imagine all kinds of weird happenings, and to long for the cheerful blaze of the kitchen fire. Then there are those lovely sunny days we get so often after snow, when the whiteness becomes pink and shimmering for a few hours before it turns to slush and every lane becomes churned-up mud.

Winter can be a grand time in the countryside, a time for sharpening wits and for keenly watching every little happening. Things and wild creatures that were hidden all summer now become exposed, and in the hedgerows the old nests stand out black.

This is the time, too, for the huddling together of bird and beast, and even of snails.

A HIDDEN WINTER STORE. (HAZEL NUTS)

Yes, John, snails gather together in groups, creep behind the loose bark of a willow or other tree in the autumn and sink into a sleep-like state for some four or five months.

They are not the only things to sleep through our worst weather, though. The hedgehog, common shrew, field-vole, dormouse and squirrel sleep, some " sound as a house " and some only fitfully, waking to take food and a breath of fresh air on a sunny mid-winter day.

Then, among other creatures which resemble the snail in that their bodies take on the temperature of the air around them—

"cold-blooded", we call them—
there are many which go into a
death-like sleep. Frogs, which
normally would soon drown if kept
for a good while under water, hibernate in the mud at the bottom of a
pond. They cease to breathe with
their lungs then, and take in air
through their skins.

RED SQUIRREL

I have sometimes found bundles
of grass-snakes coiled together
under a log for the winter. I have
heard, too, that the North American
rattlesnakes gather together in hundreds and make their way to some
long-used lair, perhaps a long distance away, and there spend the winter!

We haven't seen much in the stream lately, have we, John? That is
because in winter freshwater fish become very sleepy, cease feeding, and
make for a sheltered spot where they can conceal themselves while the
cold weather lasts.

Deep into the mud go the eels, and it is known that even frozen eels
are as lively as ever when thawed out from their ice-held mud prisons.

Birds do not sleep for the winter, as we know now, but at one time
there were many who believed that swallows stayed with us, and slept
in some warm retreats. The story most generally believed, although it
seems hard to " take in " now, is that they spent the winter in thousands
buried in the mud along with the frogs. Somehow, though, I really don't
think a swallow would change the glory of an African sky for the mud of
an English pond!

Yesterday I looked in at a huge old tithe-barn, used for storing grain,
and when my eyes became used to the dim light inside I climbed to some
of the old corner beams, and amid the masses of muck-filled cobwebs I
found what I sought. There, hung head downwards, and with bodies
overlapping, were hundreds of bats asleep for the winter, another example
of creatures that would all die if they did not have this instinct born in
them.

It was one of those crisp, bright days, however, and I was fortunate in
seeing several red squirrels scampering high in the firs and making a
welcome splash of gay movement. On a day such as this the squirrels

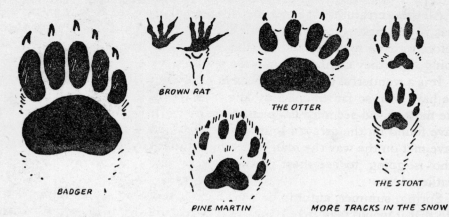

BADGER

BROWN RAT

THE OTTER

PINE MARTIN

THE STOAT

MORE TRACKS IN THE SNOW

will uncurl and, coming out of their dreys, will fling themselves about the tree-tops for an hour or two, and make raids on their stored nuts. Then back they go to sleep for another spell.

This is something the hedgehog doesn't do, however, for when he has curled himself up and rolled into a ball deep at the bottom of a hedge under a mass of autumn leaves he is there for the winter, and it is not until the spring sun shines again that he short-sightedly blinks his eyes and comes out again.

The tiny dormouse, which I think is one of the prettiest creatures we have, is " warm-blooded ", unlike snails; but as winter comes on the mechanism that controls his body-temperature ceases to act, and he would die unless he gave up the struggle to live and became cold-blooded for the winter. Curled up into a tiny ball, and deep in a cosy, warm-lined nest of moss, feathers and hair, he sleeps the winter away. I carried one in my pocket for some time, and periodically it would waken and nibble at a nut, but at other times its tiny body felt quite cold and lifeless. It was as near death then as it is possible for anything to be and still live.

Oh, and by the way, it was so mild last evening that out came several pipestrelle bats, chasing, on very feeble-looking wings, the few gnats that were also out. Very soon they crept back to the barn, however, and are now quite cold to the touch.

Turning over some stones this morning, too, I came across a toad hibernating for the winter, and in the potting-shed there are several peacock and tortoiseshell butterflies, tucked away in the corners. There they will stay until they come out in the early spring sun to give us our first glimpse of butterfly beauty.

All these creatures that go into a deep sleep all winter are like an engine that is just ticking over. Animals like the badger will eat a great deal before retiring to sleep, and use this extra fat as fuel to keep the engine going until they come out again for refilling.

It is a wonderful thing, but then isn't the whole of the world of Nature we have seen so far an amazing affair? There is some purpose for even the most trivial-seeming happening in the world of the wild, and as we have found on the caravan tour and in our walks with the characters we have met on the way the man who knows the value of stillness is the one who is going to see most of the dramas whose actors are furred or feathered.

Spring, summer, autumn or winter, England is a land so full of wild life that it would take many tours and adventures to uncover more than a fraction of its secrets. But still, already you no longer have an empty notebook. Filled as it is with your notes and sketches, you have started on the road that will lead you eventually to call yourself a " countryman ". It is a proud title, and one that has to be really earned.

Perhaps when the leaves appear again we can harness old Robby, and I will ask you to seek new adventures with the Woodman.

Goodbye for now, and very good hunting on the woodcraft trail!

INDEX

THE THAMES PUBLISHING CO.
LONDON

**DESIGNED AND PRINTED IN ENGLAND
COPYRIGHT**